WITHDRAWN

WILLIAM F. MAAG LIBRARY
YOUNGSTOWN STATE UNIVERSITY

AIChEMI MODULAR INSTRUCTION

Series E: KINETICS

Volume 3: Heterogeneous Catalysis

B. L. Crynes, Series Editor

AMERICAN INSTITUTE OF CHEMICAL ENGINEERS

© Copyright 1982

American Institute of Chemical Engineers
345 East 47th Street, New York, N.Y. 10017

Library of Congress Cataloging in Publication Data

American Institute of Chemical Engineers.
    AIChEMI modular instruction: series E, kinetics.

    Includes bibliographical references.
    Contents: v. 1. Rate of reaction, sensitivity, and chemical equilibrium.
v. 2. Reactors and rate data. v. 3. Heterogeneous catalysis.
    1. Chemical reaction, Rate of. I. Title. II. Title: Kinetics.
QD502.A43   1981   541.3′94   80-25535
ISBN 0-8169-0174-0 (v. 1)
ISBN 0-8169-0180-5 (v. 2)
ISBN 0-8169-0212-7 (v. 3)
ISSN 0270-7659

    The appearance of the code at the bottom of the first page of an article in this serial indicates the copyright owner's consent that for a stated fee copies of the article may be made for personal or internal use or for the personal or internal use of specific clients. This consent is given on the condition that the copier pay the per-copy fee (appearing as part of the code) through the Copyright Clearance Center, Inc., 21 Congress Street, Salem, Mass. 01970, for copying beyond that permitted by Sections 107 or 108 of the U.S. Copyright Law. This consent does not extend to copying for general distribution, for advertising or promotional purposes, for inclusion in a publication, or for resale.

CONTENTS

E3.1	DIFFUSION AND REACTION IN POROUS MEDIA—I	H. W. Haynes, Jr.	1
E3.2	DIFFUSION AND REACTION IN POROUS MEDIA—II	H. W. Haynes, Jr.	9
E3.3	DIFFUSION AND REACTION IN POROUS MEDIA—III	H. W. Haynes, Jr.	16
E3.4	DIFFUSION AND REACTION IN POROUS MEDIA—IV	H. W. Haynes, Jr.	24
E3.5	HEAT AND MASS TRANSFER IN PACKED BEDS—I	H. W. Haynes, Jr.	30
E3.6	HEAT AND MASS TRANSFER IN PACKED BEDS—II	H. W. Haynes, Jr.	40
E3.7	CATALYST DEACTIVATION: MECHANISMS AND KINETICS	John H. Butt	50
APPENDIX: SOLUTIONS TO THE STUDY PROBLEMS			57

Solutions to the Homework Problems are available as a separate reprint from the AIChE Educational Services Dept., 345 East 47th St., New York, NY 10017.

INTRODUCTION

In 1975 a new venture in education by and for the chemical engineering community was initiated. Prepared by the CACHE Corporation (Computer Aids for Chemical Engineering Education) and under the sponsorship of the National Science Foundation (Grant HES 75-03911), a series of small self-study fundamental concept modules for various areas of chemical engineering were commissioned, Chemical Engineering Modular Instruction, CHEMI.

It has been found in recent studies that modular study is more effective than traditional instruction in both university and continuing education settings. This is due in large measure to the discrete focus of each module, which allows the student to tailor the speed and order of his or her study. In addition, since the modules have different authors, each writing in his or her area of special expertise, they can be produced more quickly, and students may be assured of timely information. Finally, these modules have been tested in the classroom prior to their publication.

The educational effect of modular study is to reduce, in general, the number of hours required to teach a given subject; it is expected that the decreased time and expense involved in engineering education, when aided by modular instruction, will attract a larger number of students to engineering, including those who have not traditionally chosen engineering. For the practicing engineer, the modules are intended to enhance or broaden the skills he or she has already acquired, and to make available new fields of expertise.

The modules were designed with a variety of applications in mind. They may be pursued in a number of contexts: as outside study, special projects, entire university courses (credit or non-credit), review courses, or correspondence courses; and they may be studied in a variety of modes: as supplements to course work, as independent study, in continuing education programs, and in the traditional student/teacher mode.

A module was defined as a self-contained set of learning materials that covers one or more topics. It should be sufficiently detailed that an outside evaluation could identify its educational objectives and determine a student's achievement of these objectives. A module should have the educational equivalent of a one to three hour lecture.

The CHEMI Project Staff included:
E. J. Henley, University of Houston, Director
W. Heenan, Texas A & I University, Assistant Director
Steering Committee:
  L. B. Evans, Massachusetts Institute of Technology
  G. J. Powers, Carnegie-Mellon University
  E. J. Henley, University of Houston
  D. M. Himmelblau, University of Texas at Austin
  D. A. Mellichamp, University of California at Santa Barbara
  R. E. C. Weaver, Tulane University
Editors:
  Process Control: T. F. Edgar, University of Texas at Austin
  Stagewise and Mass Transfer Operations: E. J. Henley, University of Houston
  Transport: R. J. Gordon, University of Florida
  Thermodynamics: B. M. Goodwin, Northeastern University

Kinetics: B. L. Crynes, Oklahoma State University
H. S. Fogler, University of Michigan
Material and Energy Balances: D. M. Himmelblau, University of Texas at Austin
Curriculum Analysis: E. J. Henley, University of Houston

The second phase of the project, designed to fill in gaps as well as develop new modules, is under the direction of D. M. Himmelblau, University of Texas at Austin.

Volume 1 of each series will appear in 1980; Volume 2 in 1981; and so forth. A *tentative* outline of all volumes to be produced in this series follows:

SERIES E: KINETICS

Volume 1. Rate of Reaction, Sensitivity and Chemical Equilibrium

E1.1	Rate of Reaction	R. D. Williams
E1.2	Temperature Sensitivity of Rate Constants I—Arrhenius Relations	D. B. Wilson
E1.3	Temperature Sensitivity of Rate Constants II—Temperature Dependency	D. B. Wilson
E1.4	Chemical Equilibrium I	W. W. Bowden
E1.5	Chemical Equilibrium II	W. W. Bowden
E1.6	First Law of Thermodynamics Applied to Chemical Reactors I	C. C. Hsu
E1.7	First Law of Thermodynamics Applied to Chemical Reactors II	C. C. Hsu

Volume 2. Reactors and Rate Data

E2.1	Semibatch Reactors I	N. H. Chen
E2.2	Semibatch Reactors II	S. Z. Hussain
E2.3	Batch Reactors I	D. Hanesian and R. Aggarwal
E2.4	Batch Reactors II	R. G. Anthony
E2.5	Mixed Flow Reactors (Backmix, Stirred Tank)	D. Hanesian and S. Z. Hussain
E2.6	Space Times, Residence Times and Space Velocities	B. L. Crynes
E2.7	Plug Flow Reactor Mass Balances	W. C. Clements, Jr.
E2.8	Evaluation of Rate Data I	W. J. Hatcher, Jr.
E2.9	Evaluation of Rate Data II—The Differential Reactor and its Alternatives	N. Morita and H. Teshima
E2.10	Evaluation of Rate Data III	D. W. Bacon and J. Downie

Volume 3. Heterogeneous Catalysis

E3.1	Diffusion and Reaction in Porous Media I	H. W. Haynes, Jr.
E3.2	Diffusion and Reaction in Porous Media II	H. W. Haynes, Jr.
E3.3	Diffusion and Reaction in Porous Media III	H. W. Haynes, Jr.
E3.4	Diffusion and Reaction in Porous Media IV	H. W. Haynes, Jr.
E3.5	Heat and Mass Transfer in Packed Beds I	H. W. Haynes, Jr.
E3.6	Heat and Mass Transfer in Packed Beds II	H. W. Haynes, Jr.
E3.7	Catalytic Deactivation: Mechanisms and Kinetics	J. B. Butt

Volume 4. Reactor Stability and Sensitivity

E4.1	Start-Up and Transient Response of Continuous Stirred Tank Reactors in Series	D. C. Sunderberg
E4.2	Selectivity I	L. S. Kowalczyk
E4.3	Selectivity II	L. S. Kowalczyk
E4.4	Multiplicity of Steady States and Reactor Stability	R. Schmitz (NA)
E4.5	Multiplicity of Steady States and Reactor Stability	R. Schmitz (NA)
E4.6	Multiplicity of Steady States and Reactor Stability	R. Schmitz (NA)

Volume 5. Mixing Effects in Chemical Reactors

E5.1	Mixing Effects in Chemical Reactors I—Nonideal Reactors and Tracer Response Analysis	R. M. Felder and M. P. Dodukovic
E5.2	Mixing Effects in Chemical Reactors II—Models for Nonideal Reactors	R. M. Felder and M. P. Dodukovic
E5.3	Mixing Effects in Chemical Reactors III—Dispersion Model	R. M. Felder and M. P. Dodukovic
E5.4	Mixing Effects in Chemical Reactors IV—Residence Time Distributions	R. M. Felder and M. P. Dodukovic
E5.5	Mixing Effects in Chemical Reactors V—Micromixing and the Segregated Flow Model	R. M. Felder and M. P. Dodukovic
E5.6	Machine Computation of Residence Time Distribution from Tracer Test Data	T. B. Metcalfe

Modular Instruction Series

Diffusion and Reaction in Porous Media–I

H. W. Haynes, Jr.

Department of Chemical Engineering
University of Wyoming
Laramie, WY 82071

OBJECTIVES
After completing this module, the student should be able to:
1. Create equations for the various modes of mass transport in small pore systems, i.e., Knudsen diffusion, ordinary diffusion, and Poiseuille flow.
2. Combine the equations for mass transport in capillaries with a model of porous media in order to obtain order-of-magnitude estimates of the effective diffusivity.
3. Calculate effective diffusivities from data obtained in a steady-state (Wicke-Kallenbach) experiment.
4. Calculate effective diffusivities from data obtained in an unsteady-state (gas chromatography) experiment.
5. Obtain estimates of effective thermal conductivity by reference to the literature.

PREREQUISITE MATHEMATICAL SKILLS
1. Elementary calculus through differential equations.
2. Numerical integration.
3. Some knowledge of probability density functions helpful, but not required.

PREREQUISITE ENGINEERING AND SCIENCE SKILLS
1. Elementary transport phenomena—Fick's law of diffusion, Newton's law of viscosity.
2. Characterization of heterogeneous catalysts—BET surface area, pore size distributions.

The parameter most often used to characterize mass transfer in heterogeneous catalysts is the effective diffusivity. Frequently one requires only an order of magnitude estimate of this quantity, as for example, when faced with the question, Is diffusion likely to be a significant factor in the reaction? On other occasions, a quantitative estimate of the effective diffusivity is needed; for example, an engineer may wish to study the quantitative effect of coke deposition on intraparticle mass transfer.

This module begins with a discussion of the various mechanisms of mass transport in small pore systems of the type encountered in heterogeneous catalysts. How this information can be incorporated into a model of a porous catalyst is shown. Because the modeling approach cannot be relied upon for quantitative estimates, experimental methods for determining effective diffusivity will be discussed briefly. The module will end with a consideration of intraparticle heat transfer, i.e., effective thermal conductivity, since nonisothermal behavior may occur in catalytic reactions having a large heat effect.

MASS TRANSFER MECHANISMS IN CAPILLARIES

The nature of gas phase diffusion in small capillaries depends upon the magnitude of the mean free path of the diffusing molecules relative to the radius of the capillary. Under certain conditions, usually at very high pressures or in large pores, the molecular mean free path is much smaller than the pore dimensions. Wall collisions can be safely neglected, momentum is transferred by intermolecular collisions alone, and ordinary or bulk diffusion predominates. At the other extreme, at low pressures or in very small pores, the molecular mean free path is much larger than the pore dimensions. In this case the effect of intermolecular collisions can be neglected; the diffusion process is dominated by collisions with the wall; and Knudsen or free-molecule diffusion predominates. Between these two extremes a rather wide transition region exists in which both wall collisions and intermolecular collisions contribute to the diffusion process.

Ordinary diffusion can be described mathematically according to Fick's first law:

$$N_A^{(P)} = -D_{AB}\frac{dC_A}{dz} + y_A[N_A^{(P)} + N_B^{(P)}] \qquad (1)$$

This equation is written for the unidirectional diffusion of a binary relative to a stationary coordinate system. The first term on the right accounts for the diffusion of species A, and the second term accounts for the bulk motion of the fluid. In a reacting system, the relative fluxes are determined by stoichiometry; for example, if one mole of component A reacts to give one mole of component B, then $N_A^{(P)} = -N_B^{(P)}$ and the bulk flow term is zero. It can be shown on the basis of elementary kinetic theory(1) that for a dilute, hard sphere gas:

$$D_{AB} \propto \frac{T^{3/2}}{P} \tag{2}$$

The inverse relation with pressure holds well for up to about ten atmospheres for most gases; however, the temperature dependence is weak. The more accurate Chapman-Enskog theory predicts the same pressure dependence of the binary diffusivity, but the predicted exponent on the temperature term varies from about 1.65 to 2.0, a result more in agreement with experiment (2).

In the Knudsen regime, the diffusion flux of component A is given by:

$$N_A^{(P)} = -D_{KA}\frac{dC_A}{dz} \tag{3}$$

and for a cylindrical capillary, the Knudsen diffusivity derived from a simple kinetic theory approach is(1):

$$D_{KA} = \frac{2}{3}r\bar{v}_A \tag{4}$$

where r is the pore radius and $\bar{v}_A$ is the mean molecular velocity of species A; $\bar{v}_A = \sqrt{8RT/\pi M_A}$. Thus,

$$D_{KA} \propto r\sqrt{T} \tag{5}$$

From a comparison of Equations 2 and 5 it is noted that the Knudsen diffusivity is independent of pressure in contrast to the inverse pressure dependence of the ordinary diffusivity. The ordinary diffusivity is not influenced by pore geometry, whereas the Knudsen diffusivity is proportional to the pore radius.

For a two-component mixture at uniform pressure, the transition region between ordinary and Knudsen diffusion is described by:

$$N_A^{(P)} = -\frac{1}{\dfrac{1}{D_{KA}} + \dfrac{1-\alpha y_A}{D_{AB}}}\frac{dC_A}{dz} \tag{6}$$

where

$$\alpha = 1 + \frac{N_B^{(P)}}{N_A^{(P)}} \tag{7}$$

This equation can be obtained by equating the pressure forces across an element of capillary to the momentum losses incurred by molecule-molecule and molecule-wall collisions*(3,4). Equation 6 reduces to the appropriate

---

*Actually Scott and Dullien(4) obtained the correct result, Equation 6, only because of a compensating error in their derivation. [A factor $8/3\pi$ should appear as a multiplier at the Knudsen diffusivity in Equation 6.] Knudsen made the identical error in his derivation of Equation 4. The error arises from the assumption of a constant velocity pattern inherent in both derivations as discussed in Reference (5).

---

limits, Equations 1 and 3, for $\lambda \ll r$ and $\lambda \gg r$ respectively. As an approximation it has been commonplace, though not always justifiable, to neglect the concentration dependence of the transition region diffusivity, and use instead Equation 8:

$$N_A^{(P)} = -D_{TA}\frac{dC_A}{dz} \tag{8}$$

where D_{TA} is calculated from the Bosanquet equation:

$$\frac{1}{D_{TA}} = \frac{1}{D_{KA}} + \frac{1}{D_{AB}} \tag{9}$$

Strictly speaking, the Bosanquet equation is valid only for the case of equimolar counterdiffusion, or when the diffusion process is predominantly one of Knudsen diffusion.

Diffusion in multicomponent systems is complex, but nevertheless manageable. The approach normally taken in problems concerning diffusion and reaction in porous media is to define a pseudobinary diffusivity, D_{iM}, by an equation analogous to Equation 1:

$$N_i^{(P)} = -D_{iM}\frac{dC_i}{dz} + y_i\sum_{j=1}^{n}N_j^{(P)} \tag{10}$$

With this definition, the multicomponent diffusivity is given by, e.g.(6):

$$\frac{1}{D_{iM}} = \frac{N_i^{(P)}/D_{Ki} + \sum\limits_{j=1}^{n}(1/D_{ij})(y_j N_i^{(P)} - y_i N_j^{(P)})}{N_i^{(P)} - y_i\sum\limits_{j=1}^{n}N_j^{(P)}} \tag{11}$$

In the ordinary diffusion limit, $D_{Ki} \to \infty$, Equations 10 and 11 are equivalent to the well-known Stefan-Maxwell equations. The equations have been applied successfully to problems of multicomponent diffusion and reaction in porous catalysts(7) and their use is recommended for precise work. However, Equation 11 can be simplified for some cases of practical interest with the result that the calculations of diffusion and reaction are greatly simplified. Some examples are illustrated in Homework Problem 1.

Gradients in total pressure frequently arise in small pore catalysts (see Module E3.3). Under the influence of a pressure gradient, the flow of a pure gas through a capillary whose radius is small (relative to the molecular mean free path) will be Knudsen flow. No distinction can be made between Knudsen flow and Knudsen diffusion, since only species A molecules are involved in the process. At the other extreme ($\lambda \ll r$), the mass transport mechanism becomes one of viscous or Poiseuille flow. As with the diffusion case, a transition region known as the slip flow region exists between these two extremes. Mass transport, under the simultaneous influence of gradients in concentration and total pressure, is complex, but fortunately the viscous flow contribution to the total flux can be neglected with good justification in problems of diffusion and reaction in porous catalysts (see Module E3.3). This does not imply that pressure gradients are nonexistent. On the contrary, large pressure gradients are sometimes present. Homework Problem 2 seeks to verify that Equation 6 can be applied to nonisobaric systems in which the viscous flow effect can be neglected. One must not forget to correct for the pressure dependence of the transport coefficients in nonisobaric applications.

Another mode of diffusion exists in pores in which the diameter approaches molecular dimensions. This situation is frequently encountered in zeolitic diffusion. Because of strong molecule-pore wall interactions, the diffusion process is often strongly activated. Diffusivities are concentration dependent, and the rate of diffusion is influenced by the presence of other adsorbed or diffusing molecules. With zeolites, the cation location and size, and the electrostatic fields associated with the cations are all important factors. This complex mode of diffusion has been termed the "configurational" mode(8). Configurational diffusivities vary over many orders of magnitude and the only way that reliable values can be obtained is by experiment.

Surface diffusion is a little understood phenomenon that can contribute substantially to the overall mass transport in heterogeneous catalysis. It is most important in highly microporous materials. Surface diffusivities are temperature dependent, and they usually are observed to increase substantially with surface coverage. These observations are consistent with a model featuring activated jumping on a heterogeneous surface. At low coverages, the adsorbed molecules are tightly bound to high energy sites and therefore are less mobile than molecules adsorbed on low energy sites at higher coverages. For convenience, surface diffusion and gas phase diffusion rates are usually treated in an additive fashion, although recent evidence indicates that some interactions may be operative(9).

No unusual difficulties are encountered for the diffusion of liquids in large capillaries. Molecule-pore wall interactions become a factor in the region near the configurational zone. Liquid phase diffusivities are several orders of magnitude lower than gas phase values, but this effect upon the rate of diffusion is partially compensated by the higher liquid phase concentrations (and concentration gradients) as compared with gas phase concentrations. Because of the capillary condensation phenomenon, small pores can be liquid-filled at pressures considerably below the vapor pressure of the bulk liquid.

ESTIMATION OF EFFECTIVE DIFFUSIVITY FROM MODELS OF POROUS MEDIA

Now that the various mass transport processes in individual pores have been introduced, there remains the problem of incorporating these equations into a model of a porous medium. Before models can be discussed, a definition of effective diffusivity is needed:

$$N_A = -D_A^e \frac{dC_A}{dz} \tag{12}$$

It is immediately apparent from the previous section that effective diffusivities are composition dependent, except for the special cases of equimolar counterdiffusion and mass transport by Knudsen diffusion. Nevertheless, it is common practice to base calculations of diffusion and reaction in heterogeneous catalysts upon this definition, where the effective diffusivity is assumed to be independent of concentration. The errors introduced by this assumption can usually be tolerated in order of magnitude calculations.

The simplest pore structure that might be encountered is one in which all pores are of an approximately uniform size. Real pores are almost certain to be highly irregular in shape, but for convenience, we assume that the pores are cylindrical. The average pore radius, assuming cylindrical geometry, is calculated from:

$$r = \frac{2V_p}{S} \tag{13}$$

Here V_p is the total pore volume and S is the surface area, usually taken as the BET surface area. For this idealized pore structure, the diffusive flux in the porous medium can be related to the capillary diffusive flux according to:

$$N_A = \frac{\theta N_A^{(P)}}{\tau} \tag{14}$$

In this equation the porosity factor, θ, is needed to convert the flux from a pore area basis to a particle area basis. The term τ is a factor to account for deviousness of path. For an isotropic porous medium the theoretical value of τ is three, but it is sometimes treated as an empirical curve fitting parameter. If the capillary mass transport is adequately described by Equation 8, then the effective diffusivity can be estimated from:

$$D_A^e = \frac{\theta D_{TA}}{3} \tag{15}$$

Often the pore radii are not uniform, but are instead distributed about a single mean value. In this case, there is a unimodal pore size distribution or the catalyst particle is said to be unidisperse structured. Equation 13 is no longer valid and the calculations are based on the normalized pore size distribution function:

$$f_v(r) = \frac{1}{V_p} \frac{dV}{dr} \tag{16}$$

Thus, $f_v(r)dr$ represents the fraction of pore volume containing pores with radii between r and $r + dr$.

The parallel pore model provides a convenient means for applying the pore size distribution function to the effective diffusivity calculation. Visualize the porous medium as consisting of three identical bundles of straight cylindrical capillaries, only one of which is oriented in the direction of diffusion. The radius of each pore is uniform across the length of the catalyst particle and the frequency of occurrence of pores of various sizes is determined by the pore size distribution function. Upon summing the contributions from each of the properly oriented pores we obtain:

$$N_A = \frac{\theta}{3} \int_0^\infty N_A^{(P)} f_v(r) dr \tag{17}$$

where the porosity term arises in the same manner as in Equation 14 and the factor of 3 accounts for the fact that only a third of the pores have the z orientation. If we substitute from Equation 8 and make the additional assumption that mixing in a plane perpendicular to the direction of diffusion is complete, then

$$N_A = -\left[\frac{\theta}{3}\int_0^\infty D_{TA} f_v(r) dr\right] \frac{dC_A}{dz} \quad (18)$$

or

$$D_A^e = \frac{\theta}{3}\int_0^\infty D_{TA} f_v(r) dr \quad (19)$$

The quantity D_{TA} must remain in the integrand because of the dependence of the Knudsen diffusivity upon pore radius. Note that for the special case of uniform pore size, Equation 19 reduces to Equation 15. Since the cumulative pore volume curve is obtained directly from experimentation, a differentiation of the data can be avoided by substituting from Equation 16. Thus

$$D_A^e = \frac{\theta}{3V_p}\int_0^{V_p} D_{TA} dV \quad (20)$$

The experimental cumulative pore volume distribution provides the relation between pore radius and pore volume needed for the evaluation of D_{TA}.

Many heterogeneous catalysts are formed by compressing, extruding, or in some other manner compacting finely powdered microporous material into a pellet. Such catalysts contain two separate systems of pores and are said to be bidisperse structured. The micropores are due to porosity inherent in the individual microparticles of catalyst. The macropores result from voids between the microparticles after pelletization. In any realistic model of a bidisperse structured catalyst particle the separate identity of the macropore and micropore structures must be maintained, and the diffusion must be described in terms of two coefficients, an effective macropore diffusivity, $D_{A,y}^e$, and an effective micropore diffusivity, $D_{A,x}^e$. Providing that the two pore structures are composed of different size pores, both diffusivities can be obtained by integrating Equations 17 through 20 over the macropore and micropore volumes. Thus:

$$D_{A,y}^e = \frac{\theta}{3V_p}\int_{V_x}^{V_p} D_{TA} dV \quad (21)$$

and

$$D_{A,x}^e = \frac{\theta}{3(1-\theta_y)V_p}\int_0^{V_x} D_{TA} dV \quad (22)$$

where the x and y subscripts generally refer to micropore and macropore quantities respectively. The term $(1-\theta_y)$ is needed in the denominator of Equation 22 to convert the diffusive flux based upon unit area of catalyst particle to the diffusive flux based upon unit area of microparticle.

The parallel pore model of a porous medium is conceptually unrealistic, and it was presented only because of its simplicity. It is to be noted however that equivalent results can be derived from a more realistic model which assumes a random orientation of pores(10). A variety of other models of porous media have been employed for calculations of effective diffusivity, the most notable of which is the random pore model due to Wakao and Smith(11). Comparisons of the various model predictions with experimental diffusivities have indicated that the parallel pore model is at least comparable and probably superior to the others with regard to a priori estimations of effective diffusivity. With occasional exceptions the estimated values agree with experimental values to within a factor of $\pm 2(12)$. The parallel pore model is definitely superior to the other models in its ability to describe the pressure dependence of the effective diffusivity(12,13).

EXPERIMENTAL METHODS FOR DETERMINING EFFECTIVE DIFFUSIVITY

A large number of techniques have been used to measure the effective diffusivity. These include steady-state methods such as the permeability(14) and Wicke-Kallenbach(15) experiments, and unsteady-state methods such as time lag(16,17), sorption(18,19,20,21), gas chromatography(22) and frequency response(23,24) experiments. While the steady-state methods are generally less difficult to interpret, more information is provided by the unsteady-state methods. In this section the determination of effective diffusivity by the Wicke-Kallenbach and gas chromatography methods will be discussed briefly.

Wicke-Kallenbach Experiment:

The Wicke-Kallenbach apparatus, Figure 1, consists of a cylindrical (usually) sample mounted in a diffusion cell such that the opposite faces are exposed to gas streams which differ in composition. Pressures are equalized across the pellet so that mass transfer is strictly a diffusive process resulting from the imposed concentration gradient. The diffusion fluxes are calculated from a knowledge of flow rates and concentrations exiting the diffusion cell. At steady-state the diffusive flux of each species is constant and Equation 12 can be integrated across the length of the pellet to give:

$$D_A^e = \frac{N_A L}{C_{AO} - C_{AL}} \quad (23)$$

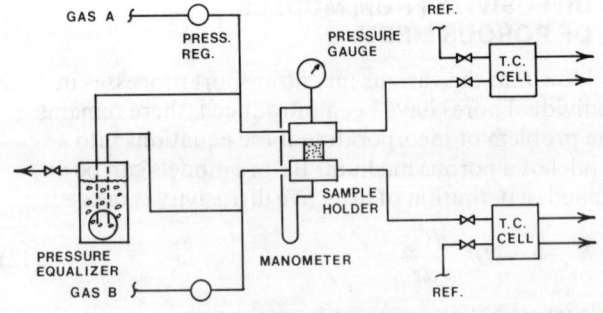

Figure 1. Wicke-Kallenbach apparatus.

where C_{AO} and C_{AL} are the concentrations at the pellet faces and L is the pellet length.

The most critical component of the Wicke-Kallenbach apparatus is the diffusion cell. The pellet must be mounted tightly in the barrier separating the two sides of the diffusion cell to prevent leakage. Stagnant layers and boundary layer resistances in series with the pellet resistance must be eliminated. Since the concentration driving force across the pellet must be known accurately, the concentrations on each side of the pellet must change only slightly as the gases flow across the pellet faces. Two designs are popular. In one, the gases are directed tangentially toward the faces of the pellet at a high flow rate. An alternative is to provide perfect mixing by adding a stirrer in both sides of the diffusion cell.

The Wicke-Kallenbach method suffers from some serious problems. Materials of construction requirements usually impose a limitation upon the maximum temperature of the measurement. Although the experimental effective diffusivity reflects diffusion in both pore systems of bidisperse structured catalysts, no means exists for experimentally separating the relative contributions of the two. On the other hand, the measurement is relatively straightforward and does not suffer from problems with equipment "speed of response," something that frequently plagues unsteady-state methods.

Gas Chromatography Experiment:

In recent years gas chromatography has emerged as a powerful tool for evaluating effective diffusivities in heterogeneous catalysts. One version of the experiment, Figure 2, consists of injecting a sample of diffusing component at the inlet to a column packed with catalyst (impulse input) and recording the effluent peak. Several methods of analysis have been employed, but two characteristics of the effluent peak are of particular interest. The first moment or mean of the chromatogram is defined by:

$$\mu = \frac{\int_0^\infty t C_A(t) dt}{\int_0^\infty C_A(t) dt} \qquad (24)$$

It contains information regarding equilibrium adsorption of the diffusing component on the catalyst surface. The second central moment or variance of the chromatogram,

$$\sigma^2 = \frac{\int_0^\infty (t - \mu)^2 C_A(t) dt}{\int_0^\infty C_A(t) dt} \qquad (25)$$

contains information regarding transport processes of both an intraparticle and interparticle nature within the column. The mean and variance are calculated by numerical integrations of the experimental chromatogram according to the above equations.

By a straightforward but tedious derivation it can be shown that the mean and variance are related to the equilibrium and mass transport parameters of a column of bidisperse structured particles by the following equations(25):

$$\mu = \frac{L}{v}[\theta_z + (1 - \theta_z)\theta_y + (1 - \theta_z)(1 - \theta_y) \\ \times \theta_x(1 + K_a)] \qquad (26)$$

$$\sigma^2 = \frac{2LD_z}{v^3}[\theta_z + (1 - \theta_z)\theta_y + (1 - \theta_z)(1 - \theta_y) \\ \times \theta_x(1 + K_a)]^2$$

$$+ \frac{2L(1 - \theta_z)[\theta_y + (1 - \theta_y)\theta_x(1 + K_a)]^2 R_y}{3vk_f}$$

$$+ \frac{2L(1 - \theta_z)[\theta_y + (1 - \theta_y)\theta_x(1 + K_a)]^2 R_y^2}{15vD_y^e}$$

$$+ \frac{2L(1 - \theta_z)(1 - \theta_y)\theta_x^2(1 + K_a)^2 R_x^2}{15vD_x^e}$$

$$+ \frac{2L(1 - \theta_z)(1 - \theta_y)^2\theta_x^2 K_a^2}{v\rho S_x k_a} \qquad (27)$$

where L is the column length, v is the superficial velocity and θ_x, θ_y and θ_z are respectively the microparticle porosity, the macropore porosity and the bed porosity. The dimensionless parameter K_a is the slope of the adsorption isotherm (assumed linear). In Equation 27 the terms contributing to the variance are in order of their appearance: a term due to axial dispersion within the packed bed, a term resulting from the external mass transfer resistance at the fluid-particle boundary, a macropore diffusion term, a micropore diffusion term, and a term due to the finite rate of adsorption. Adsorption is usually rapid relative to gas phase diffusion in which case the last term on the right of Equation 27 can be neglected. Similarly, external film mass transfer is usually fast relative to intraparticle diffusion and the term containing k_f can be dropped with little loss of accuracy. This leaves, in addition to the two effective diffusivity terms, an axial dispersion term with which to reckon.

The axial dispersion contribution to σ^2 is usually quite large and it is necessary to subtract this term out of the experimental variance in order to evaluate the effective diffusivities. One approach is to estimate D_z by undertaking a "blank" experiment over a bed of nonporous particles of the identical size and shape as those employed in the diffusivity experiment. For a bed of nonporous particles, all the terms in Equation 27, except for the first one, drop out. The axial dispersion term is computed from the blank experiment and subtracted from the experimental variance to obtain a corrected variance, σ_{xy}^2, dependent only upon the micropore and macropore diffusivity contributions.

The evaluation of K_a from the experimental first moment is straightforward. A plot of μ versus $1/v$ will result in a straight line passing through the origin. K_a is

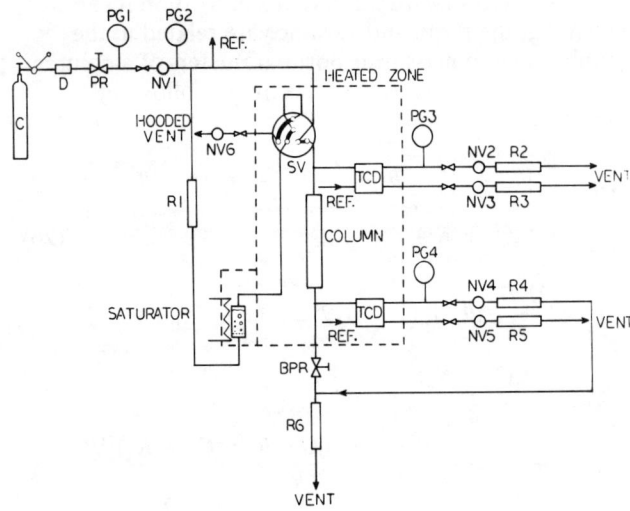

Figure 2. Gas chromatography-diffusivity apparatus.

readily calculated from the slope. Similarly, a plot of the corrected variance, σ_{xy}^2, versus $1/v$ is also a straight line passing through the origin. The slope of this plot is a sum of contributions from the micropore and macropore diffusion resistances. The relative contributions from the two pore systems can be determined by conducting experiments at two different particle sizes.

Equations 26 and 27 are based on a linear theory of gas chromatography and thus are not applicable to systems characterized by a concentration dependent diffusivity and/or a nonlinear adsorption isotherm. This problem is not as severe as it might seem however, since the pulse upon injection into the column inlet is rapidly dispersed to such an extent that diffusion and adsorption are in the low concentration linear region throughout the major portion of the column. In this event, the parameter values should be considered infinite dilution values. The chromatograms should always be checked for nonlinearities by varying the concentration of the inlet pulse.

EFFECTIVE THERMAL CONDUCTIVITY

The conduction of heat through porous catalysts occurs by a variety of mechanisms. Though attempts to model the thermal conduction process have met with some success, it is generally observed that both predicted and experimental values of λ^e, the effective thermal conductivity, fall within a surprisingly narrow range. Experimental determinations of λ^e in compacted particles result in values much smaller than the thermal conductivity of the solid material itself. For example, pellets of powdered silver have been found to have about the same thermal conductivity as alumina pellets under vacuum. The thermal resistances in the region of point contacts between compacted particles are evidently very large. Typical values of λ^e in pelleted catalysts lie in the range 5×10^{-4} to 10×10^{-4} cal/cm·s K.

NOMENCLATURE

C	=	Concentration, gmol/cc.
D_{AB}	=	Ordinary binary diffusivity, cm²/s.
D^e	=	Effective diffusivity, Equation 12, cm²/s.
D_x^e	=	Effective micropore diffusivity, cm²/s.
D_y^e	=	Effective macropore diffusivity, cm²/s.
D_{iM}	=	Pseudo binary diffusivity, Equation 11, cm²/s.
D_K	=	Knudsen diffusivity, cm²/s.
D_T	=	Diffusivity defined by Equation 9, cm²/s.
K_a	=	Adsorption equilibrium constant.
k_a	=	Adsorption rate constant, cm/s.
k_f	=	External mass transfer coefficient, cm/s.
L	=	Pellet length in Wicke-Kallenbach experiment, cm.
	=	Column length in GC diffusivity experiment, cm.
M	=	Molecular weight.
N	=	Molar flux in particle, gmol/cm²·s.
$N^{(P)}$	=	Molar flux in capillary, gmol/cm²·s.
P	=	Absolute pressure, atm.
R	=	Gas constant.
r	=	Pore radius, cm
S	=	Internal surface area, cm²/gm.
S_x	=	Surface area in micropores, cm²/gm.
T	=	Absolute temperature, K.
t	=	Time, s.
V_p	=	Total pore volume, cc/gm.
V_x	=	Micropore volume, cc micropore/gm.
v	=	Superficial velocity in column cm/s.
$\bar{v}_i$	=	Mean molecular velocity component i cm/s.
y	=	Mole fraction.
z	=	Length coordinate, cm.

Greek Letters

α	=	Quantity defined by Equation 7.
θ	=	Pellet porosity, cc void/cc pellet.
θ_x	=	Micropore porosity, cc micropore/cc microparticle.
θ_y	=	Macropore porosity, cc macropore/cc pellet.
θ_z	=	Bed porosity, cc bed void/cc bed.
λ	=	Molecular mean free path, cm.
λ^e	=	Effective thermal conductivity, cal/cm·s·K.
μ	=	Mean of normalized chromatogram, Equation 24, s.
ρ	=	Particle density, gm/cc.
σ^2	=	Variance of normalized chromatogram, Equation 25, s.
τ	=	Tortuosity factor.

LITERATURE CITED

1. Present, R. D., "Kinetic Theory of Gases," McGraw-Hill, New York (1958).
2. Bird, R. B., W. E. Stewart, and E. N. Lightfoot, "Transport Phenomena," John Wiley & Sons, New York (1960).
3. Rothfield, L. B., *A.I.Ch.E.J.* 9, 19 (1963).
4. Scott, D. S. and F. A. L. Dullien, *A.I.Ch.E.J.* 8, 113 (1962).
5. Pollard, W. G. and R. D. Present, *Phys. Rev.* 73, 762 (1948).
6. Butt, J. B., *Can. J. Ch. Eng.* 41, 130 (1963).
7. Schneider, P., *Chem. Eng. Commun.* 1, 239 (1974); 2, 155 (1966); and *Catal. Rev. Sci. Eng.* 12, 201 (1975).
8. Weisz, P. B., *Chemtech* 3(8), 498 (1973).
9. Bell, W. K. and L. F. Brown, *J. Chem. Phys.* 59, 3566 (1973).

10. Johnson, M. F. L. and W. E. Stewart, *J. Catalysis* 4, 248 (1965).
11. Wakao, N. and J. M. Smith, *Chem. Eng. Sci.* 17, 825 (1962).
12. Brown, L. F., H. W. Haynes, Jr. and W. H. Manogue, *J. Catalysis* 14, 220 (1969).
13. Satterfield, C. N. and P. J. Cadle, *Ind. Eng. Chem., Fund.* 7, 202 (1968).
14. Eberly, P. E., Jr., and D. B. Vohsberg, *Trans. Faraday Soc.* 61, 2724 (1965).
15. Wicke, E. and R. Kallenbach, *Kolloid Z.* 97, 135 (1941); See also Refs. 11 and 12.
16. Barrer, R. M., *J. Phys. Chem.* 57, 35 (1953).
17. Grachev, G. A., K. G. Ione, and A. A. Barshev, *Kinet. Katal.* 11, 541 (1970).
18. Satterfield, C. N. and A. J. Frabetti, Jr., *A.I.Ch.E. J.* 13, 731 (1967).
19. Walker, P. L., Jr., L. G. Austin, and S. P. Naudi, *Chem. Phys. Carbon* 2, 257 (1966).
20. Satterfield, C. N. and W. G. Margetts, *A.I.Ch.E. J.* 17, 295 (1971).
21. Ruckenstein, E., A. S. Vaidyanathan, and G. R. Youngquist, *Chem. Eng. Sci.* 26, 1305 (1971).
22. Sarma, P. N. and H. W. Haynes, Jr., *Adv. Chem. Ser.* 133, 205 (1974).
23. Gunn, D. J. and R. England, *Chem. Eng. Sci.* 26, 1413 (1971).
24. Koh, K. K., K. Kammermeyer, and S. T. Hwang, *Chem. Eng. Sci.* 24, 1191 (1969).
25. Haynes, H. W., Jr. and P. N. Sarma, *A.I.Ch.E. J.* 19, 1043 (1973).

SUGGESTED COMPLEMENTARY READING

1. Satterfield, C. N., "Mass Transfer in Heterogeneous Catalysis," M.I.T. Press, pp. 169–173 (1970).
2. Mason, E. A., A. P. Malinauskas, and R. B. Evans III, "Flow and Diffusion of Gases in Porous Media," *J. Chem. Phys.*, 46, 3199 (1967).
3. Johnson, M. F. L. and W. E. Stewart, "Pore Structure and Gaseous Diffusion in Solid Catalysts," *J. Catalysis*, 4, 248 (1965).
4. Wakao, N. and J. M. Smith, "Diffusion in Catalyst Pellets," *Chem. Eng. Sci.*, 17, 825 (1962).
5. Haynes, H. W., Jr. and P. N. Sarma, "A Model for the Application of Gas Chromatography to Measurements of Diffusion in Bidisperse Structured Catalysts," *A.I.Ch.E. J.* 19, 1043 (1973).

STUDY PROBLEMS

1. Suppose you are conducting an experimental determination of effective diffusivity in a heterogeneous catalyst sample and you wish to know whether the diffusion is of a predominantly Knudsen or ordinary diffusion character. What variables would you manipulate and what responses would be anticipated?

2. When is the effective diffusivity defined by Equation 12 not concentration dependent?

3. Show that the theoretical value of τ is three for an isotropic porous medium.

4. Show that for a material composed of uniform pores Equation 19 reduces to Equation 15.

5. The Wicke-Kallenbach experiment has been used by a number of investigators to test various models of mass transport in porous media. It has been commonplace to write an equation analogous to Equation 6 with "effective" Knudsen diffusivity and "effective" ordinary diffusivity replacing D_{KA} and D_{AB} respectively for application to model testing. Integrate Equation 6 for application to the Wicke-Kallenbach experiment. Why not take a similar approach to problems involving diffusion and reaction in porous catalysts, i.e. why not base such calculations on an equation of the form of Equation 6 instead of Equation 12?

6. Discuss any practical difficulties you might anticipate in evaluating second and higher moments from experimental data.

7. By reference to Equation 27 what experiments would be required to evaluate both D_x^e and D_y^e for a given catalyst.

HOMEWORK PROBLEMS

1. Obtain simplifications of Equation 11 applicable to the following limiting cases:

   a) All components except component 1 stationary.
   b) Trace amounts of components i ($i = 2,3,\ldots n$) in nearly pure component 1.
   c) All the D_{ij} the same in limit of ordinary diffusion.

2. Using the "Dusty-Gas" theory, Mason, et al(2) developed a general set of phenomenological equations describing simultaneous flow and diffusion of gases in porous media. For the special case of a binary gas mixture under isothermal conditions their results reduce to:

$$N_A = -D'_{TA}\frac{dC_A}{dz} + y_A N_T \left(\frac{D'_{TA}}{D'_{AB}}\right)$$
$$- y_A\left(1 - \frac{D'_{TA}}{D'_{AB}}\right)\frac{B'_0 P}{\mu RT}\frac{dP}{dz}$$

where:

$$\frac{1}{D'_{TA}} = \frac{1}{D'_{AB}} + \frac{1}{D'_{KA}}$$

and

$$N_T = N_A + N_B$$

and B'_0, D'_{KA} and D'_{AB} are respectively a viscous flow parameter, a Knudsen diffusivity and an ordinary diffusivity. The prime signifies that they are "effective" quantities dependent upon the geometry of the porous medium. By analogy to the equations for mass transport in capillaries, one can show that B'_0 is independent of pressure and proportional to r^2. An identical equation can be written for component B by simply interchanging subscripts.

   a) Simplify these equations in the Knudsen limit ($\lambda \gg r$) and compare with Equation 3.
   b) Simplify these equations in the hydrodynamic limit ($\lambda \ll r$) and compare with Equation 1.
   c) Write a similar equation for component B and combine the results to obtain:

$$N_B + N_A \left(\frac{D'_{KB}}{D'_{KA}}\right)$$

$$= -\frac{D'_{KB}}{RT}\left[1 + \frac{B'_0 P}{\mu}\left(\frac{y_A}{D'_{KA}} + \frac{y_B}{D'_{KB}}\right)\right]\frac{dP}{dz}$$

Under what circumstances will no pressure gradient exist?

d) Simplify these equations for negligible viscous flow effects ($B'_0/\mu = 0$) and compare with Equation 6. Comment on the constancy of the flux ratio, N_B/N_A.

e) Simplify these equations for the isobaric diffusion case and compare with Equation 6. Comment on the constancy of the flux ratio, N_B/N_A.

3. Benzene is hydrogenated over a supported metal catalyst at 250 °C and 10 atm pressure. The feed consists of benzene and hydrogen in a 1/10 benzene/hydrogen mole ratio. The catalyst has a BET surface area of 200 m²/g, a pore volume of 0.310 cc/gm and an apparent volume of 0.600 cc/g. Hudson, et al [*Trans. Faraday Soc.* 56, 1144 (1960)] report an experimental value of 0.404 cm²/s for the benzene-hydrogen diffusivity at 311 K and 1 atm pressure. Estimate the effective diffusivity for benzene.

4. The pore size distribution is determined for the catalyst of Homework Problem 3 and the cumulative pore volume curve is tabulated and shown in Table 1. Estimate the effective diffusivity for benzene.

Table 1

Pore Radius (Å)	Cumulative Pore Volume (cc/g)
21.0	0.007
23.5	0.021
26.0	0.049
28.5	0.096
31.0	0.155
33.5	0.214
36.0	0.261
38.5	0.289
41.0	0.303
∞	0.310

5. The effective diffusivity for the catalyst of Problems 3 and 4 is determined by the Wicke-Kallenbach technique. Helium and nitrogen are the diffusing gases, and the experiment is conducted at 25 °C and 1 atm pressure. At these conditions the helium effective diffusivity is 0.00260 cm²/s. Calculate the tortuosity factor. Re-estimate the benzene effective diffusivity at the conditions of Homework Problem 3.

6. Using the GC technique, Sarma [Ph.D. dissertation, U. of Mississippi, 1974] measured the effective diffusivity of helium in a commercial steam reforming catalyst. In his experiments nitrogen was the carrier and helium was the pulse gas. The results shown in Table 2 were obtained at 25 °C and 19.7 psia.

Table 2

Catalyst Particles			Blank (Nonporous) Particles	
v (cm/s)	μ (s)	σ^2 (s²)	v (cm/s)	σ^2 (s²)
2.09	51.9	338	2.53	7.45
2.97	36.8	300	2.53	7.17
3.86	27.7	178	2.97	5.23
4.31	24.8	152	3.41	4.68
4.75	22.5	130	3.85	4.12
5.19	21.3	160	4.29	3.44
5.64	18.6	98.4	4.73	2.96
6.78	16.6	102	5.17	2.65
8.14	13.1	53.9	5.61	2.23
			6.48	1.99
			7.82	1.40

Column and Catalyst Data:

$L = 152.4$ cm $\theta_x = 0.118$ $R_y = 0.650$ cm

$\theta_z = 0.420$ (0.460 for blank) $\theta_y = 0.328$

a) Assume the helium is nonadsorbed and compare values of μ calculated from Equation 26 with the experimental values.

b) Estimate the helium macropore diffusivity.

Note: Calculations indicate that the adsorption, external mass transfer, and micropore diffusion terms are all negligibly small relative to the macropore diffusion term of Equation 27 for large particles of amorphous catalysts of the type employed in this experiment [See Haynes and Sarma(25)].

Module E3.2

Diffusion and Reaction in Porous Media-II

H. W. Haynes, Jr.

Department of Chemical Engineering
University of Wyoming
Laramie, WY 82071

OBJECTIVES
Upon completion of this module, the student should be able to:
1. Quantitatively analyze isothermal, isobaric, pseudobinary systems for the effects of intraparticle diffusion on reaction rates.
2. Quantitatively analyze isothermal, isobaric, pseudobinary systems for the effects of intraparticle diffusion on reaction selectivities.

PREREQUISITE MATHEMATICAL SKILLS
1. Elementary calculus through differential equations.
2. Numerical integration and solution to ODE by the Runge-Kutta method.

PREREQUISITE ENGINEERING AND SCIENCE SKILLS
1. Mass and energy transport in porous media (Module E3.1).
2. Elementary transport phenomena—differential mass and energy balances.

In part 1 of this discussion (E3.1), the effective diffusivity was defined and estimation procedures were discussed. Here, the results of the previous section are combined with reaction kinetics and appropriate mass and energy balances to obtain a correction factor, known as the "effectiveness factor," to account for the effects of finite mass and heat transfer resistances on the observed reaction rates and selectivities.

Two types of problems are commonly encountered by chemical engineers. In the laboratory or pilot plant, where the objective is to accumulate kinetics data, the problem is to estimate the extent to which mass and heat transfer may disguise the kinetics results. We may wish simply to make a calculation to verify that we are observing the intrinsic kinetics, and an order of magnitude calculation will often suffice. In the design problem, on the other hand, it is sometimes not possible or even desirable to eliminate transport resistances. The engineer makes use of the effectiveness factor concept in order to avoid solving a second-order differential equation (boundary value problem) at every position within the reactor. For this calculation a relation between the effectiveness factor and the bulk fluid phase composition and temperature is needed.

In this module expressions will be developed for the effectiveness factors of integral reaction orders in simple pellet geometries in an isothermal, isobaric catalyst pellet. It will be shown that by appropriate definition of parameters, the results for all normal reactions (i.e. those whose rate decreases with decrease in reactant concentration) and simple geometries can be described reasonably well by a common relation. The manner in which transport effects serve to falsify the kinetics will be discussed, and the effect of intraparticle mass transfer on reaction selectivities will be considered briefly. A computer program which can be used to calculate effectiveness factors in spherical catalyst particles for an arbitrary reaction rate expression is available.*

DIFFUSION AND REACTION IN ISOBARIC, ISOTHERMAL CATALYST PARTICLES

Consider a catalyst particle characterized by the slab or flat plate geometry illustrated in Figure 1. The position corresponding to $x = 0$ is actually the central plane in a rectangular particle of thickness $2x_o$ and of infinite length, but since no net flux of component A is transferred across this plane, only one side of the particle need be considered. This model is equivalent to the "single pore" model frequently discussed in the literature. Assume that the particle surface is maintained at a reactant concentration, C_{AS}. A steady-state

---
*Program is called EFFAC, designed for use on a DEC System 10. Minimum core is 15K bytes. Language is FORTRAN IV. For a copy of the program, write the Educational Services Dept., AIChE, 345 E. 47th St., NY, NY 10017. Specify EFFAC (Module E3.2). Price of the program is $1.00.

mass balance across the differential element of particle thickness can be written:

$$-\frac{dN_A}{dx} + \rho_p R_{AW} = 0 \tag{1}$$

where R_{AW} is the molar rate of *formation* of component A per unit mass of catalyst and ρ_p is the catalyst particle density. The molar flux in the x-direction, N_A is obtained from

$$N_A = -D_A^e \frac{dC_A}{dx} \tag{2}$$

which is the definition of effective diffusivity (Equation 12 of Module E3.1). Then,

$$\frac{d}{dx}\left(D_A^e \frac{dC_A}{dx}\right) + \rho_p R_{AW} = 0 \tag{3}$$

Upon assuming that the effective diffusivity is composition independent and that the reaction can be described by nth-order kinetics, one obtains:

$$\frac{d^2C^*}{dx^{*2}} - h_x^2 C^{*n} = 0 \tag{4}$$

where C^* and x^* are dimensionless variables and h_x is a dimensionless "Thiele modulus" defined by:

$$C^* = C_A/C_{AS} \tag{5}$$

$$x^* = x/x_o \tag{6}$$

$$h_x = x_o \sqrt{\frac{\rho_p k C_{AS}^{n-1}}{D_A^e}} \tag{7}$$

The Boundary conditions are:

$$C^*(1) = 1 \tag{8}$$

$$\frac{dC^*}{dx^*}(0) = 0 \tag{9}$$

The solution of Equation 4, with boundary conditions as stated in Equations 8 and 9, is readily obtained for a first-order reaction, $n = 1$:

$$C^* = \frac{\cosh(h_x x^*)}{\cosh(h_x)} \quad n = 1 \tag{10}$$

Now define the effectiveness factor, η, as the ratio of the observed rate of reaction relative to the rate that would be observed in the absence of significant intraparticle diffusion resistances. The observed rate of reaction per unit area is given by the net flux of component A entering the pellet at the surface, $(-N_A)_S$. In the absence of diffusion limitations the entire pellet experiences the reactant concentration at the surface and the rate per unit area is $x_o \rho_p k C_{AS}^n$. Thus:

$$\eta = \frac{(-N_A)_S}{x_o \rho_p k C_{AS}^n} \tag{11}$$

Substituting from Equation 2 and writing the result in terms of dimensionless variables gives:

$$\eta = \frac{1}{h_x^2}\left(\frac{dC^*}{dx^*}\right)_S \tag{12}$$

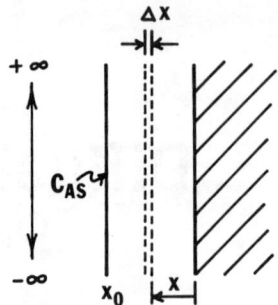

Figure 1. Slab or flat plate model of catalyst particle.

Upon differentiating Equation 10, evaluating the derivative at $x^* = 1$, and substituting the result into Equation 12, one obtains:

$$\eta = \frac{\tanh(h_x)}{h_x} \quad n = 1 \tag{13}$$

Thus, under the stated assumptions, the effectiveness factor is a unique function of the Thiele modulus, h_x. The physical significance of h_x is readily apparent from Equation 7. The Thiele modulus is the ratio of the tendency for reaction relative to that for intraparticle mass transfer. For small values of h_x mass transfer is rapid relative to the rate of reaction and the effectiveness factor approaches unity. For large values of h_x, mass transfer is slow (relative to the reaction rate) and the reaction becomes limited by mass transfer, i.e. the effectiveness factor is less than unity.

Other Pellet Geometries:

The component A mass balance in a spherical catalyst particle of radius r_o is for constant effective diffusivity and nth-order reaction:

$$\frac{d^2C^*}{dr^{*2}} + \frac{2}{r^*}\frac{dC^*}{dr^*} - h_s^2 C^{*n} = 0 \tag{14}$$

where r^* is the reduced radius,

$$r^* = r/r_o \tag{15}$$

and the Thiele modulus is given by:

$$h_s = r_o \sqrt{\frac{\rho_p k C_{AS}^{n-1}}{D_A^e}} \tag{16}$$

By following a procedure similar to the one outlined, one obtains for the effectiveness factor:

$$\eta = \frac{3}{h_s}\left[\frac{1}{\tanh(h_s)} - \frac{1}{h_s}\right] \tag{17}$$

Similarly for cylindrical pellets (closed end) of radius r_o, it can be shown that:

$$\eta = \frac{2I_1(h_c)}{h_c I_0(h_c)} \tag{18}$$

where I_k is the modified Bessel function of order k, and h_c is a Thiele modulus:

$$h_c = r_o \sqrt{\frac{\rho_p k C_{AS}^{n-1}}{D_A^e}} \tag{19}$$

For comparison, Equations 13, 17 and 18 are plotted in

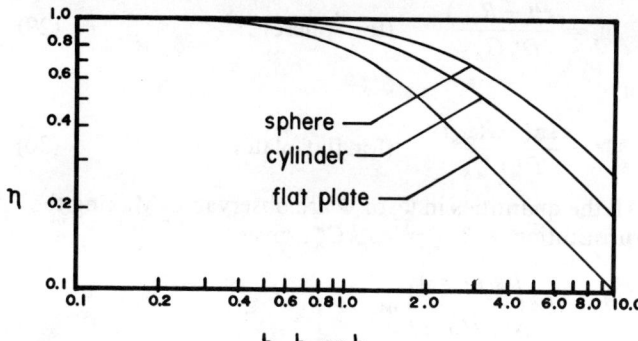

Figure 2. Effectiveness factor plot for different particle geometries.

$$\int_0^{D_{AS}^e \left(\frac{dC_A}{dx}\right)_s} \left(D_A^e \frac{dC_A}{dx}\right) d\left(D_A^e \frac{dC_A}{dx}\right)$$

$$= \int_0^{C_{AS}} D_A^e \rho_p (-R_{AW}) dC_A$$

and

$$\left(\frac{dC_A}{dx}\right)_S = \frac{\sqrt{2}}{D_{AS}^e} \left[\int_0^{C_{AS}} D_A^e \rho_p (-R_{AW}) dC_A\right]^{1/2} \quad (23)$$

where the S subscript refers to quantities evaluated at the particle external surface. Combining this result with Equations 2 and 11 gives for the effectiveness factor:

$$\eta = \frac{\sqrt{2}}{L_o \rho_p (-R_{AW,S})} \left[\int_0^{C_{AS}} D_A^e \rho_p (-R_{AW}) dC_A\right]^{1/2} \quad (24)$$

As suggested by Equation 22, define a new Thiele modulus, m, according to

$$\eta = \frac{1}{m} \quad \text{(large } m\text{)} \quad (25)$$

Thus, upon combining this definition with Equation 24, the new equation reads:

$$m = \frac{L_o \rho_p (-R_{AW,S})}{\sqrt{2}} \left[\int_0^{C_{AS}} D_A^e \rho_p (-R_{AW}) dC_A\right]^{-1/2} \quad (26)$$

Figure 2. For large values of the respective Thiele moduli, the effectiveness factor is inversely proportional to h, however, each curve is unique.

Aris was the first to point out that the results for different pellet geometries can be approximated by a single curve if the length parameter in the Thiele modulus is taken as the ratio of the pellet volume to the pellet external surface area([1]). Thus:

$$L_o = \frac{V_{\text{pellet}}}{S_{\text{ext,pellet}}} \quad (20)$$

and

$$h = L_o \sqrt{\frac{\rho_p k C_{AS}^{n-1}}{D_A^e}} \quad (21)$$

For the flat plate model $L_o = x_o$, for the spherical model $L_o = r_o/3$ and for the cylindrical model $L_o = r_o/2$. The results for the three particle geometries are replotted in Figure 3 using the Thiele modulus of Equation 21. The maximum error in approximating the spherical particle with the flat plate model (for a first-order, isothermal reaction) is about 16 percent, and for many engineering applications, an error of this magnitude can be tolerated. For values of the effectiveness factor less than about 0.1, Equations 13, 17 and 18 are well approximated by the relation:

$$\eta \cong \frac{1}{h} \quad (22)$$

Generalized Thiele Modulus:

It is possible to obtain more general results by defining still another Thiele modulus. Bischoff([2]) and Petersen([3]) recommend usage of a generalized modulus which insures that in the asymptotic limit of large h, the effectiveness factor curves will be superimposed regardless of the reaction rate form. The derivation of the modulus begins with Equation 3, which can be written as:

$$\frac{d}{dC_A}\left(D_A^e \frac{dC_A}{dx}\right)\frac{dC_A}{dx} + \rho_p R_{AW} = 0$$

In the asymptotic limit of strong intraparticle diffusion resistance, the reactant is depleted at the center of the particle, and the gradient in concentration is zero, as required by Equation 9. Thus:

At this point, no assumption has been made about the reaction rate form, nor has it been required that the effective diffusivity be independent of concentration. Furthermore, since the flat plate model approximates other particle geometries, the effectiveness factors calculated from Equations 25 and 26 are exact for all particle geometries for large m.

To illustrate the advantages of this approach, consider the case of constant effective diffusivity and nth-order kinetics. Equation 26 becomes:

$$m = \frac{L_o \rho_p k C_{AS}^n}{\sqrt{2}} \left[D_A^e \rho_p k \int_0^{C_{AS}} C_A^n dC_A\right]^{-1/2}$$

Upon evaluating the integral and utilizing the definition

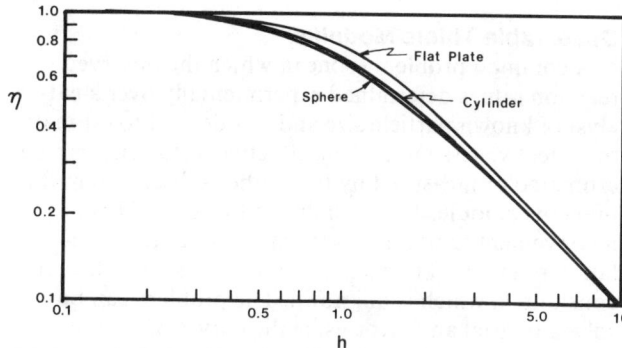

Figure 3. Effectiveness factor plot for different particle geometries using length parameter of Equation 20.

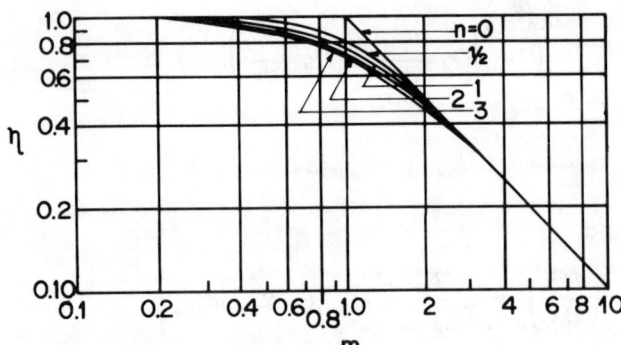

Figure 4. General effectiveness factor plot for simple order reactions(2).

of Equation 21 there is obtained:

$$m = h\sqrt{\frac{n+1}{2}} \quad n > -1 \quad (27)$$

The effectiveness factors for an nth-order reaction in a slab can be obtained by solving Equation 4 with the boundary conditions in Equations 8 and 9 and then substituting the results into Equation 12. The results of this computation for several values of n are plotted versus the modulus m in Figure 4. A reasonable approximation of the effectiveness factor plots for all positive reaction orders can be illustrated by the use of a single curve. The maximum spread between third-order and half-order kinetics is about 15 percent. Thus an estimate of the effectiveness factor can be obtained for arbitrary kinetics by calculating m using Equation 26 and then substituting this result into:

$$\eta = \frac{\tanh(m)}{m} \quad (28)$$

which is the solution for $n = 1$ (i.e., Equation 13 with m replacing h_x).

This procedure should be used with caution for complex kinetics expressions. Negative reaction orders can give rise to effectiveness factors greater than unity, a result which is not consistent with Equation 28. For the same reason, the procedure is of little practical use in application to nonisothermal particles. For these systems, the generalized Thiele modulus should only be used in the limit of strong intraparticle diffusion resistance.

Observable Thiele Modulus:

A common problem is one in which the observed reaction rate is determined experimentally over a catalyst of known particle size and it is desired to estimate the effectiveness factor. The effective diffusivity can be estimated or measured by the methods discussed in the previous module. The modulus of Equation 21 is inconvenient to use in this situation, since its calculation requires a knowledge of the intrinsic reaction rate constant, k, which is unknown. The problem can be solved by trial and error using the curves of Figures 2–4; however, this can be eliminated by defining a new modulus according to:

$$\Phi_s = \frac{r_o^2(-R_{obs})}{D_A^e C_{AS}} \quad \text{(for sphere)} \quad (29)$$

or

$$\Phi = \frac{L_o^2(-R_{obs})}{D_A^e C_{AS}} \quad \text{(for flat plate)} \quad (30)$$

All the quantities in Φ_s or Φ are observable. Making the substitution $-R_{obs} = \eta \rho_p k C_{AS}^n$ gives:

$$\Phi = L_o^2 \left(\frac{\rho_p k C_{AS}^{n-1}}{D_A^e} \right) \eta$$

or

$$\Phi = h^2 \eta \quad (31)$$

and similarly:

$$\Phi_s = h_s^2 \eta \quad (32)$$

Thus a plot of η versus Φ can be constructed from the graph of η versus h. An example of such a plot is given in Figure 2 of Module E3.3.

Some Characteristics of Diffusion Limited Reactions:

From the definition of η, it follows that the observed reaction rate is given by $-R_{obs} = \eta \rho_p k C_{AS}^n$ for nth-order kinetics. In the asymptotic limit of strong intraparticle diffusion resistance, one finds that $-R_{obs} = \rho_p k C_{AS}^n / m$, or after substituting from Equations 27 and 21:

$$-R_{obs} = k_{obs} C_{AS}^{(n+1)/2} \quad (33)$$

where

$$k_{obs} = \frac{1}{L_o}\sqrt{\frac{2\rho_p k D_A^e}{n+1}} \quad (34)$$

The temperature dependence of the rate constant k is given by the Arrhenius relation. If the diffusion is considered to be activated, then Equation 34 requires that the observed activation energy be:

$$E_{obs} = \frac{1}{2}(E_a + E_d) \quad (35)$$

where E_a and E_d are activation energies for reaction and diffusion, respectively. Since diffusion is a physical process, the activation energy is characteristically small, relative to the activation energy for chemical reaction (an exception is diffusion in zeolites, which may be characterized by activation energies of up to 20 kcal/gmol and higher). Thus:

$$E_{obs} \cong \frac{1}{2} E_a \quad (36)$$

A telltale indication of significant intraparticle diffusion resistances is a break in the slope of the Arrhenius plot for an observed rate constant in accord with Equation 36. See Figure 5. At low temperatures, the reaction rate is slow relative to the rate of diffusion, the Thiele modulus is small, the effectiveness factor approaches unity and the observed activation energy is the same as the true activation energy, E_a. As the temperature is increased, the rates increase exponentially and a range of temperatures exists in which a transition to the strong intraparticle diffusion mode takes place. At this point the observed activation energy is halved. The kinetics of the reaction are also falsified in the strong pore diffusion regime, for $n \neq 1$. Thus a true zero-order reaction appears as half-order, a true second-order reaction appears as three-halves order, etc. Note that pore diffusion can never "control" the rate of reaction since the observed results are always dependent upon the intrinsic reaction kinetics.

EFFECT OF MASS TRANSFER ON REACTION SELECTIVITY

As an example of the extent to which intraparticle diffusion can affect reaction selectivity, consider the first-order reaction system,

$$A \xrightarrow{k_1} B \xrightarrow{k_2} C$$

and suppose that component B is the desired product. An example may be the production of gasoline (B) from a heavy gas oil (A) where some light gases (C) are also produced. Wheeler terms this problem a Type III selectivity problem(4).

We will analyze the problem using flat plate geometry. The component A mass balance has already been solved and the dimensionless component A concentration profile is given by Equation 10.

$$C_A^* = \frac{\cosh(h_A x^*)}{\cosh(h_A)} \quad (10)$$

In a similar manner, the following is obtained from the component B mass balance:

$$C_B^* = \frac{\cosh(h_B x^*)}{\cosh(h_B)} + \frac{h_B^2 SR}{h_B^2 - h_A^2}$$

$$\times \left[\frac{\cosh(h_A x^*) \cosh(h_B) - \cosh(h_B x^*) \cosh(h_A)}{\cosh(h_B) \cosh(h_A)} \right]$$

(37)

where:

$$h_A = x_o \sqrt{\rho_p k_1 / D_A^e} \quad (38)$$

$$h_B = x_o \sqrt{\rho_p k_2 / D_B^e} \quad (39)$$

$$S = k_1 / k_2 \quad (40)$$

$$R = C_{AS} / C_{BS} \quad (41)$$

The point selectivity, Δ, is defined as the observed relative rate of formation of B to the observed rate of disappearance of A. In all but perfectly mixed reactors the parameter R will vary with position inside the reactor, hence the term "point" selectivity. Thus

$$\Delta = \frac{(N_B)_S}{(-N_A)_S} \quad (42)$$

Substituting from Equation 2 for N_A and from the analogous equation for N_B in terms of dimensionless quantities, Δ is:

$$\Delta = -\frac{h_A^2 \left(\frac{dC_B^*}{dx^*}\right)_S}{h_B^2 SR \left(\frac{dC_A^*}{dx^*}\right)_S} \quad (43)$$

Differentiating Equations 10 and 37, evaluating the derivatives at $x^* = 1$ and substituting into Equation 43 gives:

$$\Delta = \left[\frac{h_A h_B}{h_B^2 - h_A^2} - \frac{h_A}{SRh_B} \right] \frac{\tanh(h_B)}{\tanh(h_A)} - \frac{h_A^2}{h_B^2 - h_A^2}$$

(44)

Considerable simplification of this expression results in the asymptotic limit of strong pore diffusion resistance and for the case $D_A^e = D_B^e$.

$$\Delta = \frac{\sqrt{S}}{\sqrt{S} + 1} - \frac{1}{R\sqrt{S}} \quad (45)$$

It is of interest to compare this result with the situation in which pore diffusion resistances are absent. In which case,

$$\overline{\Delta} = \frac{R_B}{-R_A} = \frac{k_1 C_{AS} - k_2 C_{BS}}{k_1 C_{AS}}$$

or

$$\overline{\Delta} = 1 - \frac{1}{RS} \quad (46)$$

The ratio of these two expressions is:

$$\Delta / \overline{\Delta} = \left(\frac{\sqrt{S}}{\sqrt{S} + 1} \right) \left(\frac{RS - 1 - \sqrt{S}}{RS - 1} \right). \quad (47)$$

Since both terms in parenthesis are less than unity it follows that intraparticle diffusion resistance always serves to lower the point selectivity to product B. This

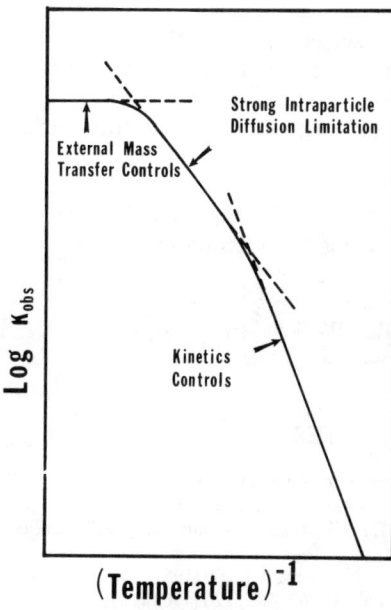

Figure 5. Arrhenius plot under different mass transfer regimes.

should also be apparent intuitively. Component B once formed must be removed from the interior of the catalyst quickly in order to prevent further reaction to component C, making rapid mass transfer essential for the formation of B in high yields.

NOMENCLATURE

C	=	Concentration, gmol/cc.
C^*	=	Dimensionless concentration, Equation 5.
D^e	=	Effective diffusivity, cm²/s.
E_a	=	True activation energy, cal/gmol.
E_d	=	Activation energy for diffusion, cal/gmol.
E_{obs}	=	Observed activation energy, cal/gmol.
h	=	Thiele modulus, Equation 21.
h_c	=	Thiele modulus, Equation 19.
h_s	=	Thiele modulus, Equation 16.
h_x	=	Thiele modulus, Equation 7.
k	=	Rate constant.
L_o	=	Length parameter, Equation 20.
m	=	Thiele modulus, Equation 26.
N	=	Molar flux, gmol/cm²·s.
n	=	Reaction order.
R	=	Concentration ratio, Equation 41.
r	=	Length coordinate, spherical particle model, cm.
	=	Length coordinate, cylindrical particle model, cm.
r^*	=	Dimensionless length coordinate, Equation 15.
R	=	Reaction rate, gmol/cc·s.
R_{AW}	=	Molar rate of formation of component A, gmol/g·s.
S	=	Selectivity, Equation 40.
S_{ext}	=	Particle external surface area, cm².
V_{pellet}	=	Particle volume, cc.
x	=	Length coordinate, flat plate model, cm.
x^*	=	Dimensionless length coordinate, flat plate model, Equation 6.

Greek Letters

Δ	=	Point selectivity, Equation 42.
$\overline{\Delta}$	=	Point selectivity for rapid intraparticle diffusion.
η	=	Effectiveness factor based upon surface properties.
ρ_p	=	Particle density, g/cc.
Φ	=	Thiele modulus, Equation 30.
Φ_s	=	Thiele modulus, Equation 29.

Subscripts

A	=	Component A.
obs	=	Observed.

LITERATURE CITED

1. Aris, R., *Chem. Eng. Sci.* 6, 262 (1957).
2. Bischoff, K. B., *AIChE J* 11, 351 (1965).
3. Petersen, E. E., "Chemical Reaction Analysis," Prentice-Hall (1965).
4. Wheeler, A., *Adv. Catalysis* 3, 250 (1951).
5. Satterfield, et al, *AIChE J* 15, 226 (1969).
6. Weisz, P. B. and E. W. Swegler, *J Phys. Chem.* 823 (1955).

SUGGESTED COMPLEMENTARY READINGS

1. Satterfield, C. N., "Mass Transfer in Heterogeneous Catalysis," M.I.T. Press, pp. 129–163 (1970).
2. Wheeler, A., "Reaction Rates and Selectivity in Catalyst Pores," *Adv. Catal. III*, 249 (1951).

STUDY PROBLEMS

1. Show that Equation 22 approximates Equations 13, 17 and 18 for large values of h. For what values of h is this approximation reasonable?

2. We have defined three Thiele moduli: h, m and Φ. Discuss the utility of each.

3. Discuss the physical significance of the Thiele modulus.

4. Under what circumstances does the calculation of catalyst effectiveness become independent of particle geometry? Explain.

5. When are calculations using the generalized Thiele modulus, m, likely to be in error? When are these calculations most precise?

6. What is the basis for the observed rate of reaction for use in Equations 29 or 30, i.e. R_{obs} = rate per unit?

HOMEWORK PROBLEMS

1. In a pilot plant study utilizing very small catalyst particle sizes it was determined that $\rho_p k = 0.248$ cc/cc·s for the first-order reaction. Varying particle size had no effect upon k in the pilot plant study. Estimate the catalyst effectiveness factor in a commercial unit utilizing 1/4 inch catalyst spheres. The catalyst is exposed to the same reaction environment in the pilot plant and commercial reactors. The effective diffusivity is estimated to be 0.02 cm²/s.

2. The gas phase reaction $A \rightarrow B$ is studied in a backmix reactor at 100 atm and 500 K. The reactor is charged with 10 grams of spherical catalyst particles (particle diameter – 0.6 cm, particle density – 1.2 gm/cc). When pure A is fed to the reactor at a rate of 7.0 liters (STP) per hour, 90% is converted into product. Varying the stirrer speed has no effect upon conversion. Assume the particle is isothermal. The effective diffusivity is estimated to be 5×10^{-4} cm²/s.

   a) Can we safely neglect external mass and heat transfer effects? Why?
   b) Estimate the effectiveness factor assuming that the reaction is first order and irreversible.

3. Satterfield, et al(5), measured rates of hydrogenation of α-methylstyrene (AMS) over a Pd/Al$_2$O$_3$ catalyst at 50 °C and atmospheric pressure in a well-stirrer batch reactor. The reactor, which contained six spherical catalyst pellets, was charged with 1800 grams of pure AMS. The reaction mixture was sampled periodically over a three-hour period and analyzed for the hydrogenation product, cumene.

Table 1.

r_o(cm)	C_{AS}/C_{BS}	$-R_A \times 10^5$	$R_B \times 10^5$	$R_C \times 10^5$
0.184	185	5.7	1.81	3.1
0.310	312	4.2	1.11	2.4

The measured reaction rate was 3.42×10^{-7} mol/s·cc pellet. Calculations indicated that external mass transfer resistances could be neglected.

a) Assume the reaction is first-order in both H_2 and α-methylstyrene, and estimate the effectiveness factor.

b) Experiments were also conducted with powdered catalysts (<40 microns), and it was shown that in these experiments the effectiveness factor was unity. The reaction rate at 50 °C and 1 atm pressure was 5.96×10^{-5} mol/s·cc catalyst. Calculate the effectiveness factor for the full-size particles using this additional information and compare with the results of part (a). Comment on the discrepancies between the experimental and calculated values of the effectiveness factor.

Additional data:
H_2 solubility in AMS = 3.54×10^{-6} mol/cc.
Catalyst porosity = 0.498.
Range of pore diameters = 120–180Å.
Catalyst particle diameter = 0.825 cm.
Diffusivity of H_2 in AMS = 1.65×10^{-4} cm²/s.
Self-diffusivity of AMS (est.) = 2.3×10^{-5} cm²/s.
Density of AMS = 0.914 g/cc.

4. The catalytic dehydrogenation of cyclohexane to cyclohexene and benzene was studied over a chromia-alumina catalyst in a differential reactor experiment(6). Reaction rate data at two particle sizes (spheres) is reproduced in Table 1, where the subscripts A, B, and C refer to cyclohexane, cyclohexene, and benzene respectively. The rates are in some gmol/g·min. The reactor was designed for highly turbulent flow; consequently external heat and mass transfer resistances may be neglected. Diffusion is the Knudsen region. For the analysis below assume that all reactions are first order in hydrocarbon concentration and irreversible.

   a) Neglect intraparticle diffusion effects and calculate the selectivity ratio, $S = k_1/k_2$, where k_1 and k_2 are the respective first order rate constants for disappearance of cyclohexane and cyclohexene. Do this for both particle sizes and compare. Comment.
   b) Make the same calculation in part (a), but taking into account intraparticle diffusion. Estimate the effectiveness factor at each particle size. Compare the results with the results of part (a).

5. The reaction $A \rightarrow$ Products is carried out in the presence of a heterogeneous catalyst in a differential flow reactor. The average component A concentration within the reactor is $C_A = 0.025$ gmol/L. The reaction kinetics are described by the following rate expression:

$$-R_{AW} = \frac{kC_A^2}{1 + K_A C_A} \quad \frac{\text{gmol}}{\text{g} \cdot \text{s}}$$

where $k = 12$ L²/gmol·g·s and $K_A = 100$ L/gmol at reaction temperature. The spherical catalyst particle is isothermal and external transport resistances are negligible. Estimate the effectiveness factor by
a) using the generalized Thiele modulus, and by
b) numerical solution of the component A mass balance.

Additional data:

$r_0 = 0.12$ cm = Radius of spherical catalyst particles.

$\rho_p = 1.2$ g/cc = Catalyst particle density.

$D_A^e = 0.20$ cm²/s = Component A effective diffusivity.

Repeat the calculations for $k = 120$ L²/gmol·g·s.

Diffusion and Reaction in Porous Media-III

H. W. Haynes, Jr.

Department of Chemical Engineering
University of Wyoming
Laramie, WY 82071

OBJECTIVES
Upon the completion of this module, the student should be able to:
1. Quantitatively analyze nonisothermal, nonisobaric, multicomponent systems for the effects of intraparticle diffusion on reaction rates.

PREREQUISITE MATHEMATICAL SKILLS
1. Elementary calculus through differential equations.
2. Numerical integration and solution to ODE by the Runge-Kutta method.

PREREQUISITE ENGINEERING AND SCIENCE SKILLS
1. Mass and energy transport in porous media—Module E3.1.
2. Application of the effectiveness factor concept and the various Thiele moduli to isothermal systems—Module E3.2
3. Elementary transport phenomena—differential mass and energy balances.

This module treats the more complex problems of diffusion and reaction in porous media which involve gradients in temperature and pressure. Also shown, is how the restriction to binary systems can be removed. In nonisothermal problems, the differential energy balance is solved simultaneously with the reactant mass balance, giving rise to a linear relation between reactant concentration and temperature. This simplifies the problem greatly. Next, a relationship is derived between the total pressure and the reactant concentration for a binary with volume change. Substantial pressure gradients are sometimes present, but even in these circumstances, the viscous flow contribution to the molar flux can be safely neglected. Finally, this module covers the case of multicomponent diffusion and reaction in heterogeneous catalysts and presents a computer program for calculating the generalized Thiele modulus in these systems.

DIFFUSION AND REACTION IN NONISOTHERMAL CATALYST PARTICLES

In the presence of a large heat effect, significant temperature gradients may exist within the catalyst particle. The reactant mass balance across a differential element of a slab particle was obtained in Module E3.2:

$$-\frac{dN_A}{dx} + \rho_p R_A w = 0 \qquad (1)$$

where:

$$N_A = -D_A^e \frac{dC_A}{dx} \qquad (2)$$

The analogous energy balance is:

$$-\frac{dq}{dx} + \rho_p R_A w(-\Delta H_r) = 0 \qquad (3)$$

where q is the heat flux which can be obtained from Fourier's Law of heat conduction,

$$q = -\lambda^e \frac{dT}{dx} \qquad (4)$$

and ΔH_r is the heat of reaction per mole of component A. The effective thermal conductivity, λ^e, was discussed in Module E3.1.

The mass and energy balances, Equations 1 and 3 can be combined to eliminate the reaction rate term:

$$\frac{dq}{dx} + (-\Delta H_r)\frac{dN_A}{dx} = 0$$

Since there is no net flux of mass or heat at the center of the particle, this expression can be integrated to give:

$$\int_0^q dq + (-\Delta H_r)\int_0^{N_A} dN_A = 0$$

or

$$q + (-\Delta H_r)N_A = 0$$

Substituting from Equations 2 and 4 for the fluxes and integrating for constant D_A^e:

$$-\lambda^e \int_{T_S}^{T} dT - (-\Delta H_r) D_A^e \int_{C_{AS}}^{C_A} dC_A = 0$$

or

$$T = T_S + \frac{(-\Delta H_r) D_A^e}{\lambda^e} (C_{AS} - C_A) \quad (5)$$

Observe that the temperature is linearly related to reactant concentration. In deriving Equation 5 it has been assumed that the transport coefficients and the heat of reaction are independent of temperature and concentration. Notice that no assumption has been made regarding the form of the rate expression. Furthermore, it can be shown that this result is valid for any particle geometry. Equation 5 is the well-known Prater relation(1). An upper bound on the intraparticle temperature can be obtained by setting the reactant concentration within the particle equal to zero. Thus,

$$\frac{T_{max} - T_S}{T_S} = \beta \quad (6)$$

where β is a dimensionless parameter defined as:

$$\beta = \frac{(-\Delta H_r) D_A^e C_{AS}}{\lambda^e T_S} \quad (7)$$

A final equation is needed to account for temperature dependence of the rate constant. This is the Arrhenius relation:

$$k = k_o \exp(-E_a/RT) \quad (8)$$

The mass balance, the Prater relation and the Arrhenius equation provide a complete solution to the problem.

For spherical particle geometry, the reactant balance can be combined with Equations 5 and 8 to give:

$$\frac{d^2 C^*}{dr^{*2}} + \frac{2}{r^*} \frac{dC^*}{dr^*} - h_s^2 C^{*n} \exp\left[\frac{\gamma \beta (1 - C^*)}{1 + \beta(1 - C^*)}\right] = 0 \quad (9)$$

where the rate constant in the definition of h_s, Equation 16 of Module E3.2, is evaluated at the particle surface and γ is a dimensionless parameter sometimes referred to as the Arrhenius number.

$$\gamma = E_a/RT_S \quad (10)$$

Weisz and Hicks(2) solved Equation 9 for $n = 1$ with the boundry conditions

$$C^*(1) = 1 \quad (11)$$

$$\frac{dC^*}{dr^*}(0) = 0 \quad (12)$$

using the numerical procedure programmed in E3.2.

For nonisothermal reactions, the effectiveness factor is defined as the ratio of the observed rate of reaction to that which would occur if the pellet interior were all exposed to reactant at the *same concentration and temperature* as that existing at the outside pellet surface.

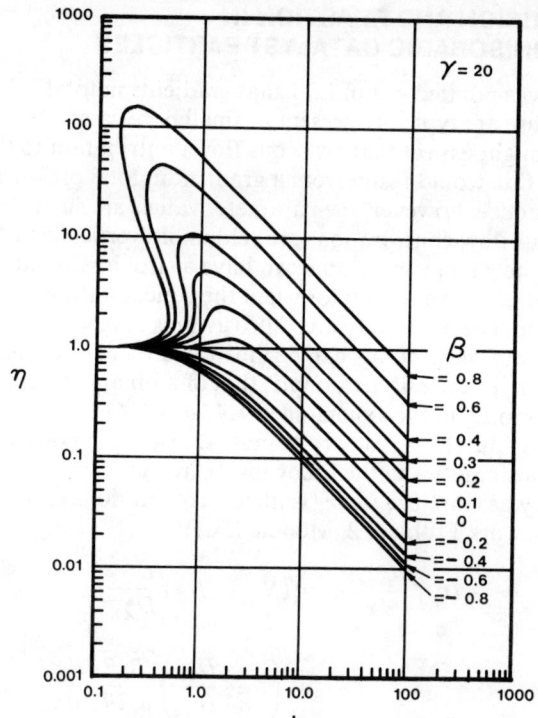

Figure 1. Effectiveness factor plot for nonisothermal first-order reaction in a sphere(2).

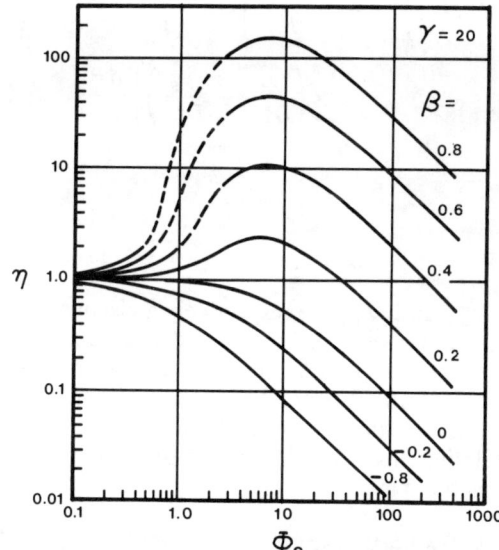

Figure 2. Effectiveness factor versus the observable Thiele modulus. Nonisothermal first-order reaction in a sphere(2).

It is apparent from this definition that effectiveness factors greater than unity can be realized for exothermic reactions. Weisz and Hicks presented their numerical results in terms of both h_s and Φ_s. Two of their plots are reproduced in Figures 1 and 2. For highly exothermic reactions, multiple steady states are possible, but the parameter values required to achieve such results are rather extreme and will seldom be encountered in practice(3).

Modular Instruction Series

DIFFUSION AND REACTION IN NONISOBARIC CATALYST PARTICLES

It was pointed out in E3.1 that gradients in total pressure are typically present in small pore catalysts. One might expect that a viscous flow contribution to the mass flux would result from a gradient in total pressure. In practice, however, the parameter values are such that viscous flow contributions are seldom if ever realized. Still, the change in volume can have a strong influence on the effectiveness factor when the concentration dependence of the effective diffusivity is taken into account. These points can be illustrated by considering the simplest possible example, that of a binary system conforming to the stoichiometry $A \to \nu B$ (4).

The "dusty-gas" theory of mass transport in porous media simplifies to the following expressions for a binary gas mixture under isothermal conditions (See Homework Problem 2, Module E3.1):

$$N_A = -D_{TA}^e \frac{dC_A}{dx} + y_A(N_A + N_B)\frac{D_{TA}^e}{D_{AB}^e}$$

$$- y_A \left(1 - \frac{D_{TA}^e}{D_{AB}^e}\right)\frac{B_o^e P}{\mu RT}\frac{dP}{dx} \quad (13)$$

and

$$N_B + N_A \left(\frac{D_{KB}^e}{D_{KA}^e}\right) = -\frac{D_{KB}^e}{RT}\left[1 + \frac{B_o^e P}{\mu}\right.$$

$$\left. \times \left(\frac{y_A}{D_{KA}^e} + \frac{y_B}{D_{KB}^e}\right)\right]\frac{dP}{dx} \quad (14)$$

where

$$\frac{1}{D_{TA}^e} = \frac{1}{D_{AB}^e} + \frac{1}{D_{KA}^e} \quad (15)$$

and B_o^e, D_{KA}^e and D_{AB}^e are respectively a viscous flow parameter, a Knudsen diffusivity and an ordinary diffusivity. The "e" superscript signifies that they are "effective" quantities dependent upon the structural characteristics of the porous medium.

The relative fluxes are established by the reaction stoichiometry. Thus,

$$\nu N_A + N_B = 0 \quad (16)$$

Also, stoichiometry dictates that the molecular weights of A and B must be related according to $M_A = \nu M_B$. Since the Knudsen diffusivity is inversely proportional to the square root of molecular weight, it follows that:

$$\frac{D_{KB}^e}{D_{KA}^e} = \sqrt{\nu} \quad (17)$$

Equations 13, 15 and 16 can be combined to give:

$$N_A = -D_{Tr}^e \frac{dC_A}{dx} - \frac{y_A B_o^e P D_{Tr}^e}{\mu RT D_{KA}^e}\frac{dP}{dx} \quad (18)$$

where

$$\frac{1}{D_{Tr}^e} = \frac{1}{D_{KA}^e} + \frac{1-(1-\nu)y_A}{D_{AB}^e} \quad (19)$$

Similarly, when we eliminate N_B between Equations 14 and 16 we have

$$\left(\frac{D_{KB}^e}{D_{KA}^e} - \nu\right) N_A = -\frac{D_{KB}^e}{RT}\left[1 + \frac{B_o^e P}{\mu}\left(\frac{y_A}{D_{KA}^e} + \frac{y_B}{D_{KB}^e}\right)\right]\frac{dP}{dx}$$

$$(20)$$

Now eliminate N_A between Equations 18 and 20, collect the coefficients of $(dC_A)/(dx)$ and $(dP)/(dx)$ and divide both sides of the resulting equation by $(dP)/(dx)$ to obtain:

$$\frac{dC_A}{dP} = \frac{D_{KB}^e}{\left(\frac{D_{KB}^e}{D_{KA}^e} - \nu\right) RT D_{Tr}^e}$$

$$\times \left[1 + \frac{B_o^e P}{\mu}\left(\frac{y_A}{D_{KA}^e} + \frac{y_B}{D_{KB}^e}\right)\right] - \frac{y_A B_o^e P}{\mu RT D_{KA}^e}$$

$$(21)$$

This equation is more conveniently expressed in terms of dimensionless variables:

$$\frac{dC^*}{dP^*} = \frac{1}{y_S(1-\sqrt{\nu})}\left\{1 + \frac{1 + P^* - (1-\nu)y_S C^*}{\beta}\right\}$$

$$\times \left\{1 + \frac{\gamma}{\mu^*}\left[y_S C^* + \frac{1 + P^* - y_S C^*}{\sqrt{\nu}}\right]\right\} - \frac{\gamma C^*}{\mu^*}$$

$$(22)$$

where:

$$C^* = C_A/C_{AS} \quad (23)$$

$$P^* = (P - P_S)/P_S \quad (24)$$

$$y_S = C_{AS}RT/P_S \quad (25)$$

$$\mu^* = \mu/\mu_A \quad (26)$$

and in the present context β and γ are dimensionless parameters given by:

$$\beta = D_{AB,S}^e/D_{KA}^e \quad (27)$$

$$\gamma = B_o^e P_S/\mu_{AS} D_{KA}^e \quad (28)$$

It is to be noted that just as the Prater relation between temperature and reactant concentration is valid for all rate forms and particle geometries, so is Equation 22 for the relation between pressure and reactant concentration generally valid.

The viscosity of a gas mixture is a complex function of component concentrations and so it is necessary to resort to numerical methods for the solution to Equation 22. Equation 22 with the initial condition $C^*(0) = 1$ was solved by the Runge-Kutta method, and the

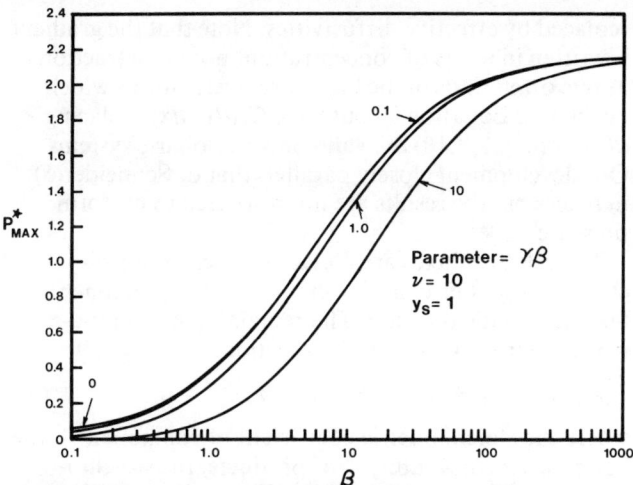

Figure 3. Maximum pressure drop in catalyst particle. $A \to \nu B$.

maximum pressure drop for a range of parameter values is plotted in Figure 3 [The viscosity of the mixture was calculated using the Wilke Equation(5)]. It is clear that in the ordinary diffusion limit ($\beta \to 0$) no pressure gradient exists within the particle; whereas, in the Knudsen limit ($\beta \to \infty$), the maximum pressure differential is observed.

If one calculates values of $\gamma\beta$ using realistic values of the transport coefficients, it quickly becomes apparent that values of this quantity far removed from zero are impossible. Using simple kinetic theory to estimate the transport coefficients it can be shown that $\gamma\beta = 0.11$ [see Homework Problem 2]. These results then confirm the statement made earlier regarding the lack of importance of the viscous flow term.

In what follows it will be assumed that the viscous flow term can be neglected, i.e. that $\gamma = 0$. Equation 22 then simplifies to a linear form:

$$\frac{dC^*}{dP^*} = \frac{1}{y_S(1 - \sqrt{\nu})} \left\{ 1 + \frac{1 + P^* - (1 - \nu)y_S C^*}{\beta} \right\} \quad (29)$$

which can be solved analytically. The solution is:

$$y_S C^*(1 - \nu) = P^* + \beta + 1 - \frac{\beta}{1 + \sqrt{\nu}} + \left[y_S(1 - \nu) - (1 + \beta) + \frac{\beta}{1 + \sqrt{\nu}} \right] \exp\left[-\frac{1 + \sqrt{\nu}}{\beta} P^* \right] \quad (30)$$

An upper bound on the intraparticle pressure is obtained by setting $C^* = 0$.

$$P^*_{max} + \beta + 1 - \frac{\beta}{1 + \sqrt{\nu}} + \left[y_S(1 - \nu) - (1 + \beta) + \frac{\beta}{1 + \sqrt{\nu}} \right] \exp\left[-\frac{1 + \sqrt{\nu}}{\beta} P^*_{max} \right] = 0 \quad (31)$$

This equation is plotted in Figure 3 for comparison with the numerical calculations.

Consider the following two methods for calculating effectiveness factors in the presence of a significant change in volume. In the rigorous approach, the flux given by Equation 18 is substituted into Equation 1 or an analogous mass balance for other particle geometries. As already demonstrated the second term in Equation 18 can be eliminated with little loss of accuracy. The resulting differential equation for spherical particle geometry and nth order reaction kinetics is:

$$\frac{d^2C^*}{dr^{*2}} + \frac{2}{r^*}\frac{dC^*}{dr^*} - \left[\frac{\frac{dP^*}{dC^*} - (1 - \nu)y_S}{P^* + \beta + 1 - (1 - \nu)y_S C^*} \right] \left(\frac{dC^*}{dr^*} \right)^2$$
$$- [P^* + \beta + 1 - (1 - \nu)y_S C^*] h_s^2 C^{*n} = 0 \quad (32)$$

The pressure and pressure derivative as functions of concentration are obtained from Equation 30 and 29 respectively.

In the limit of ordinary or bulk diffusion ($\beta = 0$) no pressure gradient exists within the particle and Equation 32 simplifies to:

$$\frac{d^2C^*}{dr^{*2}} + \frac{2}{r^*}\frac{dC^*}{dr^*} + \left[\frac{(1 - \nu)y_S}{1 - (1 - \nu)y_S C^*} \right] \left(\frac{dC^*}{dr^*} \right)^2$$
$$- [1 - (1 - \nu)y_S C^*] h_s^2 C^{*n} = 0 \quad (33)$$

This problem was solved by Weekman and Gorring(6) who presented their results in terms of a correction to the effectiveness factor calculation in which the effects of change in volume are neglected. One of Weekman and Gorring's plots is reproduced in Figure 4.

The second method of estimating the effectiveness factor when volume changes are significant makes use of the generalized modulus of Equation 26, Module

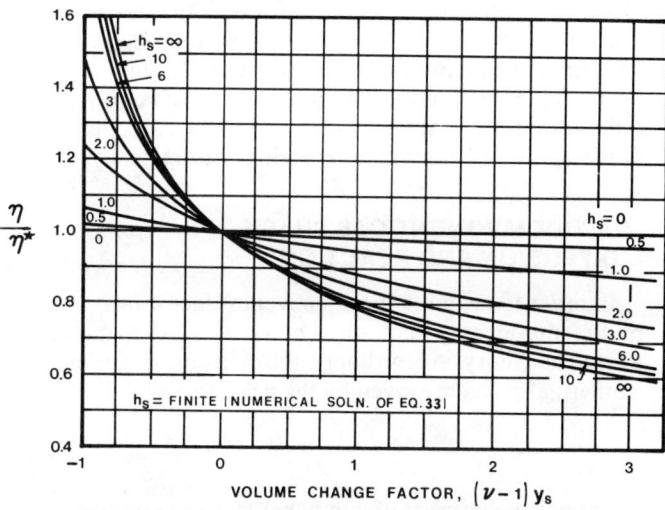

Figure 4. Effect of volume change on effectiveness factor for first-order reaction in ordinary diffusion regime. Spherical particles(6).

E3.2. Again one considers the nth order reaction ($n > 0$) and neglects the viscous flow contribution to mass transfer. The effective diffusivity is then given by D^e_{Tr}, Equation 19. Substituting into the definition of the generalized Thiele modulus:

$$m = \frac{L_o \rho_p k C^n_{AS}}{\sqrt{2}} \left\{ \int_0^{C_{AS}} \left[\frac{1}{\frac{1}{D^e_{KA}} + \frac{1 - (1-\nu)y_A}{D^e_{AB}}} \right] \right.$$

$$\left. \times \rho_p k C^n_A dC_A \right\}^{-1/2} \quad (34)$$

Or, in terms of dimensionless quantities:

$$m = \frac{h}{\sqrt{2I}} \quad (35)$$

where:

$$I = \int_0^1 \frac{C^{*n} dC^*}{P^* + \beta + 1 - (1-\nu)y_S C^*} \quad (36)$$

and P^* is calculated from Equation 30. The integral of Equation 36 will in general require a numerical evaluation. However, when mass transport is by ordinary diffusion ($\beta = 0$), the integral simplifies to

$$I = \int_0^1 \frac{C^{*n} dC^*}{1 - (1-\nu)y_S C^*} \quad (37)$$

which is a standard form for integer values of n. These two methods of computation are illustrated in Homework Problem 3.

Weekman also analyzed reaction in the nonisothermal catalyst particle with volume change in the bulk diffusion limit(7). Volume change was found to have a profound effect on exothermic reactions, with volume contraction causing large increases in effectiveness and volume expansion greatly reducing effectiveness relative to the constant volume case. Volume change had little effect on the effectiveness factor for endothermic reactions. Weekman's analysis takes into account the temperature dependence of the transport coefficients and heat of reaction, but except for the region of large γ and β the results are practically identical to the solutions based upon temperature independent parameters.

MULTICOMPONENT GAS PHASE DIFFUSION AND REACTION

In order to evaluate the effectiveness factor in a multicomponent system, one again makes use of the dusty-gas theory. Accordingly, the diffusive fluxes in an isothermal pellet are given by the n equations:

$$-\frac{dC_i}{dx} = \frac{N_i}{D^e_{Ki}} + \sum_{j=1}^{n} \frac{y_j N_i - y_i N_j}{D^e_{ij}}, \quad i = 1, n \quad (38)$$

where n is the number of components in the mixture. This equation is identical to Equations 10 and 11 of Module E3.1 except that fluid phase diffusivities are replaced by effective diffusivities. Note that the gradient is written in terms of concentration, not mole fractions, as one often finds in the literature. Derivations which begin with Equation 38 but have $C_T(dy_i/dx)$ replacing dC_i/dx (e.g. 8,9,10) are valid only in isobaric systems. Our development closely parallels that of Schneider(8) in places but the results are not restricted to uniform pressure.

The relative fluxes are dictated by reaction stoichiometry. Let us consider that r of the n components take part in the reaction. The remaining $n-r$ components are inert. Consider the reaction:

$$A_1 + \nu_2 A_2 + \nu_3 A_3 + \ldots + \nu_r A_r = 0 \quad (39)$$

where the stoichiometric coefficient of component 1, the key component, is unity. For products, the stoichiometric coefficients are negative. For each component that participates in the reaction the molar flux of component i is related to the key component flux by:

$$N_i = \nu_i N_1 \quad i = 1, r \quad (40)$$

The inert components are stationary. Thus

$$N_i = 0 \quad i = r+1, n \quad (41)$$

Upon substituting for the component fluxes in Equation 38, one obtains:

$$-\frac{dC_i}{dx} = N_1 \left[\frac{\nu_i}{D^e_{Ki}} + \sum_{j=1}^{r} \frac{y_j \nu_i - y_i \nu_j}{D^e_{ij}} + \nu_i \sum_{j=r+1}^{n} \frac{y_j}{D^e_{ij}} \right] \quad (42)$$

for $i = 1, r$ and

$$-\frac{dC_i}{dx} = -N_1 y_i \sum_{j=1}^{r} \frac{\nu_j}{D^e_{ij}} \quad (43)$$

for $i = r+1, n$.

From the inverse pressure dependence of the ordinary diffusivity (Module E3.1, Equation 2) and the ideal gas law:

$$D^e_{ij} = D^e_{ij,S} \left(\frac{P_S}{P} \right) \quad (44)$$

and

$$y_i = \frac{RTC_i}{P} \quad (45)$$

where the subscript S refers to quantities evaluated at the pellet surface. Substituting into Equations 42 and 43:

$$-\frac{dC_i}{dx} = N_1 \left\{ \frac{\nu_i}{D^e_{Ki}} + \frac{RT}{P_S} \left[\sum_{j=1}^{r} \frac{C_j \nu_i - C_i \nu_j}{D^e_{ij,S}} + \nu_i \sum_{j=r+1}^{n} \frac{C_j}{D^e_{ij,S}} \right] \right\} \quad (46)$$

where $i = 1, r$; and

$$-\frac{dC_i}{dx} = -N_1 \left\{ \frac{RTC_i}{P_S} \sum_{j=1}^{r} \frac{\nu_j}{D^e_{ij,S}} \right\} \quad (47)$$

where $i = r + 1, n$. Now Equation 46 can be written for the key component:

$$-\frac{dC_1}{dx} = N_1 \left\{ \frac{1}{D^e_{K1}} + \frac{RT}{P_S} \left[\sum_{j=1}^{r} \frac{C_j - C_1 \nu_j}{D^e_{1j,S}} + \sum_{j=r+1}^{n} \frac{C_j}{D^e_{1j,S}} \right] \right\} \quad (48)$$

divide this result into each of the Equations 46 and 47 to obtain:

$$\frac{dC_i}{dC_1} = \frac{\frac{\nu_i}{D^e_{Ki}} + \frac{RT}{P_S} \left[\sum_{j=1}^{r} \frac{C_j \nu_i - C_i \nu_j}{D^e_{ij,S}} + \nu_i \sum_{j=r+1}^{n} \frac{C_j}{D^e_{ij,S}} \right]}{\frac{1}{D^e_{K1}} + \frac{RT}{P_S} \left[\sum_{j=1}^{r} \frac{C_j - C_1 \nu_j}{D^e_{1j,S}} + \sum_{j=r+1}^{n} \frac{C_j}{D^e_{1j,S}} \right]} \quad (49)$$

where $i = 1, r$ and

$$\frac{dC_i}{dC_1} = -\frac{\frac{RTC_i}{P_S} \sum_{j=1}^{r} \frac{\nu_j}{D^e_{ij,S}}}{\frac{1}{D^e_{K1}} + \frac{RT}{P_S} \left[\sum_{j=1}^{r} \frac{C_j - C_1 \nu_j}{D^e_{1j,S}} + \sum_{j=r+1}^{n} \frac{C_j}{D^e_{1j,S}} \right]} \quad (50)$$

$i = r + 1, n$

Equations 49 and 50 constitute $n-1$ first-order ordinary differential equations relating the concentrations of all components of the mixture to the key component. Note that no assumptions have been made regarding the form of the rate expression nor has any particular particle geometry been assumed. The viscous flow contribution to the total flux has been neglected, but in view of the results of the previous section, this simplification appears justified. For known surface concentrations these equations are readily solvable by standard numerical techniques. A computer program employing the fourth-order Runge-Kutta algorithm is available.*

As an example let us consider the cyclopropane hydrogenolysis reaction problem analyzed by Schneider(8):

$$\text{cyclo} - C_3H_6 + H_2 \xrightarrow{Pd/Al_2O_3} C_3H_8$$

The reaction takes place at 20 °C and 1 atm total pressure. Some experiments were conducted in the presence of nitrogen (inert). Letting A_1 = cyclopropane, A_2 = hydrogen, A_3 = propane and A_4 = nitrogen, we have the binary diffusivities for each gas pair (Table 1).

---

*Program is called CONREL, and is designed for use on a DEC System 10. Language is FORTRAN. For a copy of the program, write Educational Services, AIChE, 345 E. 47th St., NY, NY 10017. Specify CONREL (Module E3.3). Price of the program is $1.20.

Table 1. Binary diffusion coefficients.

Pair	1–2	1–3	1–4	2–3	2–4	3–4
D_{ij} (cm²/s)	0.464	0.063	0.121	0.434	0.737	0.112

The Knudsen diffusivities calculated for a catalyst particle whose average pore radius is 836Å are listed in Table 2.

Table 2. Knudsen diffusion coefficients.

Component	1	2	3
D_{Ki} (cm²/s)	0.214	0.978	0.209

The diffusivities in Tables 1 and 2 are converted to effective diffusivities by multiplying by a geometric factor (see Equation 15 of Module E3.1). Assume that the geometric factors for Knudsen diffusion and ordinary diffusion are the same and are equal to 0.1.

This problem is solved for the case $C_{1S} = 0.0300$ gmol/L, $C_{2S} = 0.01157$ gmol/L, $C_{3S} = 0$ and $C_{4S} = 0$, using the computer program and computational results that are available for this module.* The problem was solved for other values of C_{1S} ($C_{3S} = C_{4S} = 0$, $P_S = 1$ atm). The pressures corresponding to $C_1 = 0$, i.e. total (key) reactant consumption, are plotted in Figure 5. These pressures therefore represent the minimum pressures possible within the catalyst particle for the specified external concentrations. The curves in Figure 5 for different values of pore radius cover the transition from Knudsen diffusion dominating to ordinary diffusion dominating. In the Knudsen diffusion region the pressure variation within the pellet will be greatest. It is also apparent from an inspection of Equations 49 and 50 that the C_i's are linear functions of C_1 in the Knudsen diffusion region.

In Figure 5 the maximum deviation from the external pressure is observed at a value of $C_{1S} \cong 0.034$ gmol/L. This point corresponds to the simultaneous exhaustion of both reactants. Schneider refers to the corresponding surface concentrations as the "diffusion stoichiometric mixture," because at complete conversion the system does not contain any reactants. To the right of the diffusion stoichiometric mixture composition in Fig-

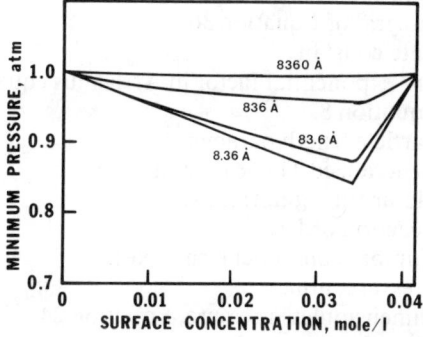

Figure 5. Maximum pressure drop for cyclopropane hydrogenolysis problem ($P_S = 1$ atm, $C_{3S} = C_{4S} = 0$).

ure 5, the key component is exhausted before reactant 2. Computations in this region are accomplished merely by changing key components.

Calculations of catalyst effectiveness are readily carried out using the generalized Thiele modulus. The effective diffusivity is defined according to:

$$N_1 = -D_1^e \frac{dC_1}{dx} \tag{51}$$

Comparing with Equation 48, one has:

$$\frac{1}{D_1^e} = \frac{1}{D_{K1}^e} + \frac{RT}{P_S}\left[\sum_{j=1}^{r} \frac{C_j - C_1\nu_j}{D_{1j,S}^e} + \sum_{j=r+1}^{n} \frac{C_j}{D_{1j,S}^e}\right] \tag{52}$$

Upon substitution into Equation 26 of module E3.2 we have:

$$m = \frac{L_o \rho_p (-R_{1W,S})}{\sqrt{2}}$$

$$\times \left\{ \int_0^{C_{1s}} \frac{\rho_p(-R_{1w})dC_1}{\frac{1}{D_{K1}^e} + \frac{RT}{P_S}\left[\sum_{j=1}^{r} \frac{C_j - C_1\nu_j}{D_{1j,S}^e} + \sum_{j=r+1}^{n} \frac{C_j}{D_{1j,S}^e}\right]} \right\}^{-1/2} \tag{53}$$

The numerical evaluation of m is easily accomplished once the C_i's are known at equally spaced intervals of C_1. In the available computer program, m is calculated after Equations 49 and 50 are solved. Simpson's rule is employed to evaluate the integral in Equation 53.

NOMENCLATURE

- B_o^e = Viscous flow parameter, cm².
- C = Concentration, gmol/cc.
- C^* = Dimensionless concentration, Equation 23.
- D_1^e = Effective diffusivity defined by Equation 51, cm²/s.
- D_{ij}^e = Effective ordinary diffusivity, cm²/s.
- D_{Ki}^e = Effective Knudsen diffusivity, cm²/s.
- D_{TA}^e = Effective diffusivity defined by Equation 15, cm²/s.
- D_{Tr}^e = Effective diffusivity defined by Equation 19, cm²/s.
- E_a = Activation energy, cal/gmol.
- h_s = Thiele modulus.
- I = Integral of Equation 36.
- k = Rate constant.
- k_o = Pre-exponential factor in Arrhenius equation, Equation 8.
- L_o = Particle length parameter.
- m = Generalized Thiele modulus.
- N = Molar flux, gmol/cm²s.
- n = Reaction order.
- = Number components in mixture.
- P = Pressure, atm.
- P^* = Dimensionless pressure, Equation 24.
- q = Heat flux, cal/cm² s.
- R = Gas constant.
- r = Number reacting components.
- r^* = Dimensionless length coordinate, spherical particle geometry.
- R_{AW} = Molar rate of formation of component A, gmol/g·s.
- T = Temperature, K.
- x = Length coordinate, flat plate model, cm.
- y = Mole fraction.

Greek Letters
- β = Adiabatic temperature rise, Equation 7.
- = Transport Parameter, Equation 27.
- γ = Arrhenius number, Equation 10.
- = Transport parameter, Equation 28.
- ΔH_r = Heat of reaction, cal/gmol.
- η = Effectiveness factor based upon surface properties.
- η^* = Effectiveness factor neglecting change in volume.
- λ^e = Effective thermal conductivity, cal/cm·s K.
- μ = Viscosity, gm/s·cm.
- μ^* = Dimensionless viscosity, Equation 26.
- ν = Stoichiometric coefficient.
- ρ_p = Particle density, g/cc.

Subscripts
- i = component i (= A,B, or integer).
- S = Surface quantity.

LITERATURE CITED

1. Prater, C. D., *Chem. Eng. Sci.* 8, 284 (1958).
2. Weisz, P. B. and J. S. Hicks, *Chem. Eng. Sci.* 17, 265 (1962).
3. Satterfield, C. N., "Mass Transfer in Heterogeneous Catalysis," pp. 167–168, M.I.T. Press, Cambridge, Mass. (1970).
4. Kehoe, J. P. G. and R. Aris, *Chem. Eng. Sci.* 28, 2094 (1973).
5. Wilke, C. R., *J. Chem. Phys.* 18, 517 (1950).
6. Weekman, V. W., Jr. and R. L. Gorring, *J. Catalysis* 4, 260 (1965).
7. Weekman, V. W., Jr., *J. Catalysis* 5, 44 (1966).
8. Schneider, P., *Chem. Eng. Commun.* 1, 239 (1974); *Catal. Rev.-Sci. Eng.* 12, 201 (1975).
9. Hite, R. H. and R. Jackson, *Chem. Eng. Sci.* 32, 703 (1977).
10. Butt, J. B., *Can. J. Chem. Eng.* 130 (1963).

SUGGESTED COMPLEMENTARY READING:

1. C. N. Satterfield, "Mass Transfer in Heterogeneous Catalysis," pp. 164–207, M.I.T. Press (1970).
2. Schneider, P., "Intraparticle Diffusion in Multicomponent Catalytic Reactions," *Catal. Rev.-Sci. Eng.* 12, 201 (1975).

STUDY PROBLEMS

1. Summarize the equations needed for calculations of diffusion and reaction in nonisothermal catalyst particles (constant effective diffusivity).

2. Under what circumstances can the effectiveness factor be greater than unity?

3. Under what circumstances are significant pressure gradients likely to exist within a catalyst particle?

4. When is it necessary to consider viscous transport effects in calculations of diffusion and reaction in porous catalysts?

5. In what respects are the concentration relations, Equations 49 and 50 analogous to the Prater relation, Equation 5?

6. How would you calculate the effectiveness factor using Equation 53? What would be the limitations on this approach?

HOMEWORK PROBLEMS

1. Consider Homework Problem 2 of Module E3.2. In addition to the information given in the original problem statement, it is determined from thermochemical tables that the heat of reaction is $-10,000$ cal/gmol. The effective thermal conductivity is estimated to be 1×10^{-3} cal/s·cm K. Can we safely assume that the pellet is isothermal? Show by calculation.

2. Use simple kinetic theory expressions for the transport coefficients to estimate the product $\gamma\beta$, (Equations 27 and 28), and comment on the importance of viscous transport in calculations of diffusion and reaction in heterogeneous catalysts. Note that the viscous flow parameter $B_o = r^2/8$ in circular capillaries.

3. A first-order, irreversible gas phase reaction takes place in a backmix reactor charged with spherical catalyst particles. The catalyst pores are sufficiently large that it can be safely assumed that the mass transport mechanism is one of ordinary diffusion. The reaction stoichiometry is $A \rightarrow 5B$, and the feed is pure A. Estimate the effectiveness factor when the reactor is operating at the 15% conversion level using a) the curves of Figure 4 and b) the generalized Thiele modulus.

Additional data:

r_o = Catalyst particle radius = 0.125 cm.
D_A^e = Effective diffusivity = 0.25 cm²/s.
$\rho_p k$ = First-order rate constant per unit particle volume = $576\ s^{-1}$.

4. Use the computer program available for Module E3.2 to verify several points on Figures 1 and 2.

Diffusion and Reaction in Porous Media–IV

H. W. Haynes, Jr.

Department of Chemical Engineering
University of Wyoming
Laramie, WY 82071

OBJECTIVES
Upon completion of this module, the student should be able to:
1. Calculate effectiveness factors based upon bulk fluid conditions in the presence of finite external heat and mass transfer resistances.
2. Apply convenient diagnostic criteria to a heterogeneous catalytic system in order to identify significant heat and mass transfer limitations with a minimum of calculation.
3. Provide a physical rational for multiple steady state solutions to problems involving finite heat and mass transfer resistances.

PREREQUISITE MATHEMATICAL SKILLS
1. Elementary calculus through differential equations.
2. Numerical integration and solution to ODE by the Runge-Kutta method.
3. Solutions to nonlinear algebraic equations by iterative techniques.

PREREQUISITE ENGINEERING AND SCIENCE SKILLS
1. Mass and energy transport in porous media (Module E3.1).
2. Application of the effectiveness factor concept and the various Thiele moduli to non-isothermal systems (Modules E3.2 and E3.3).
3. Elementary transport phenomena—differential mass and energy balances.

In the foregoing discussion of diffusion and reaction in porous media, it has been implicitly assumed that the catalyst surface concentrations and temperatures are identical to corresponding values in the bulk fluid surrounding the particle. There are situations in which this assumption is invalid; problems of finite external transport resistances will be treated in this module.

After the discussion of external transport effects a brief survey of handy "diagnostic criteria" will be presented. These criteria are useful for establishing the importance of the various inter- and intraparticle transport effects in kinetics experiments.

EXTERNAL HEAT AND MASS TRANSFER EFFECTS

For the analysis of external transport effects in packed bed reactors it is customary to define convective mass and heat transport coefficients according to:

$$N_A = k_c(C_{AS} - C_{AB}) \tag{1}$$

and

$$q = h_c(T_S - T_B) \tag{2}$$

In actuality, the local transport coefficients vary somewhat from point-to-point on the particle surface(*1*); however, if the problem is to be kept tractable, there is little choice but to rely upon the "particle average" values of the transport coefficients defined by Equations 1 and 2. In addition to Equations 1 and 2, one can write for the mass and heat transfer fluxes at the surface:

$$N_A = -D_A^e \left(\frac{dC_A}{dx}\right)_S \tag{3}$$

$$q = -\lambda^e \left(\frac{dT}{dx}\right)_S \tag{4}$$

Upon equating fluxes and writing the results in terms of dimensionless variables, there is obtained:

$$\frac{dC^*}{dx^*}(1) = N_{Bi_m}\left(\frac{C_{AB}}{C_{AS}} - 1\right) \tag{5}$$

and

$$\frac{dT^*}{dx^*}(1) = N_{Bi_h}\left(\frac{T_B}{T_S} - 1\right) \tag{6}$$

where the S subscripted quantities are external surface

values and the B subscripted quantities are bulk fluid values. The dimensionless quantity

$$N_{Bi_m} = \frac{x_o k_c}{D_A^e} \tag{7}$$

is a mass transfer Biot number. Similarly,

$$N_{Bi_h} = \frac{x_o h_c}{\lambda^e} \tag{8}$$

is a heat transfer Biot number. The Biot number, N_{Bi}, is a measure of the relative rates of interphase and intraphase transport.

To analyze systems described by power law kinetics and slab particle geometry, recall from previous discussions that the reactant mass balance is given by:

$$\frac{d^2 C^*}{dx^{*2}} - h^2 C^{*n} = 0 \tag{9}$$

and similarly, the energy balance is:

$$\frac{d^2 T^*}{dx^{*2}} - \beta h^2 C^{*n} = 0 \tag{10}$$

One approach to the problem is to seek a solution to Equations 9 and 10 using the boundary conditions, Equations 5 and 6, along with:

$$\frac{dC^*}{dx^*}(0) = 0 \tag{11}$$

and

$$\frac{dT^*}{dx^*}(0) = 0 \tag{12}$$

This method of solution is general, but the computations are sometimes lengthy. Furthermore, with this approach it is not possible to utilize the vast amount of information on systems for which external transport is infinitely rapid. Fortunately, a different method of solution can be followed in practical situations. Assume that the particle is bathed in a fluid of uniform concentration and temperature. For most situations involving symmetrical particle geometry, the concentrations and temperature at the surface must also be uniform (but unknown). Thus the boundary conditions:

$$C^*(1) = 1 \tag{13}$$

and

$$T^*(1) = 1 \tag{14}$$

are still applicable and the solutions presented in our previous discussions can be utilized.

Before discussing a method of solution it should be noted that if the particle is nonsymmetric, e.g. a finite cylinder, the intraparticle gradients normal to the surface will be nonuniform and Equations 5 and 6 require that the surface concentration and temperature also be nonuniform. Sometimes it is possible to observe asymmetrical solutions in symmetrical particles. For example, if a two-sided slab is operating under conditions such that multiple steady states are possible, then there is no reason to assume that the two faces are at the same steady state. Further details can be found in Aris(2). Finally, notice that if the catalyst particle is located in a region of the reactor where sharp gradients exist, then the fluid surrounding the particle may not be uniform in concentration and temperature(3). With these possible exceptions, the assumption of uniform surface quantities is reasonable. To assume otherwise would introduce such complications into reactor design calculations that the problem would likely remain unsolvable. Furthermore, any refinement of this assumption would hardly seem warranted in view of other approximations in the analysis.

To continue with an analysis of the power law kinetics problem, assume that relations of the form

$$\eta = \eta(n, h, \beta, \gamma) \tag{15}$$

(as in Figure 1 of Module E3.3) are available and applicable to the problem. When external transport resistances are finite, it is convenient to utilize a new effectiveness factor, η', defined as the ratio of the observed rate of reaction to the rate that would be observed if particle concentrations and temperature were uniform and equal to values in the bulk fluid. Thus, for an nth-order reaction:

$$\eta' = \frac{k_c(C_{AB} - C_{AS})}{x_o \rho_p k_B C_{AB}^n} \tag{16}$$

where the prime (′) refers to quantities based on bulk fluid conditions. The effectiveness factor relative to particle surface conditions can be written:

$$\eta = \frac{k_c(C_{AB} - C_{AS})}{x_o \rho_p k_S C_{AS}^n} \tag{17}$$

From a comparison of these two expressions it is apparent that:

$$\eta' = \eta \left(\frac{k_S}{k_B}\right) \left(\frac{C_{AS}}{C_{AB}}\right)^n \tag{18}$$

(The temperature dependence of the transport coefficients is small in comparison to the rate constants and can be neglected in typical applications). Equation 17 is easily rearranged to give:

$$\frac{N_{Bi_m}}{h'^2}\left(1 - \frac{C_{AS}}{C_{AB}}\right) = \eta \left(\frac{k_S}{k_B}\right)\left(\frac{C_{AS}}{C_{AB}}\right)^n \tag{19}$$

where h' is the Thiele modulus written in terms of bulk fluid properties, i.e.:

$$h' = x_o \sqrt{\frac{\rho_p k_B C_{AB}^{n-1}}{D_A^e}} \tag{20}$$

upon comparing this definition with Equation 7 of Module E3.2, the relation is:

$$h = h'(k_S/k_B)^{1/2}(C_{AS}/C_{AB})^{(n-1)/2} \tag{21}$$

In a similar manner, the relation for the energy flux at the surface can be written:

$$q = h_c(T_S - T_B) = (-\Delta H_r)\eta x_o \rho_p k_S C_{AS}^n$$

and this equation after rearrangement becomes:

$$\frac{N_{Bi_h}}{\beta' h'^2}\left(\frac{T_S}{T_B} - 1\right) = \eta \left(\frac{k_S}{k_B}\right)\left(\frac{C_{AS}}{C_{AB}}\right)^n \tag{22}$$

with

$$\beta' = \frac{(-\Delta H_r)D_A^e C_{AB}}{\lambda^e T_B} \quad (23)$$

Comparing this result with Equation 7 of Module E3.3 allows one to write:

$$\beta = \beta' \left(\frac{T_B}{T_S}\right)\left(\frac{C_{AS}}{C_{AB}}\right) \quad (24)$$

Finally, an expression is needed for the temperature dependence of the reaction rate constant. From the Arrhenius relation it follows that:

$$\frac{k_S}{k_B} = \exp\left[-\gamma'\left(\frac{T_B}{T_S} - 1\right)\right] \quad (25)$$

where

$$\gamma' = E_a/RT_B \quad (26)$$

or upon combining with Equation 10 of Module E3.3:

$$\gamma = \gamma'(T_B/T_S) \quad (27)$$

Table 1 summarizes the necessary relations for calculating the effectiveness factor for an nth-order reaction in the presence of significant internal and external heat and mass transport resistances. In a design problem, the six quantities n, h', β', γ', N_{Bi_m}, and N_{Bi_h} are known, and the unknown quantities are T_S, C_{AS}, k_S, h, β, γ, η, η'. Solving for η' will generally require trial and error computations, but simplifications are possible in some instances. For example, the equations reduce to:

$$\eta' = \frac{\tanh(h')}{h'[1 + h' \tanh(h')/N_{Bi_m}]} \quad (28)$$

for the case of an isothermal first-order reaction (slab geometry).

Table 1. Equations applicable to design problems involving finite external heat and mass transport resistances

Equation	Number
$\frac{N_{Bi_m}}{h'^2}\left(1 - \frac{C_{AS}}{C_{AB}}\right) = \eta\left(\frac{k_S}{k_B}\right)\left(\frac{C_{AS}}{C_{AB}}\right)^n$	(19)
$\frac{N_{Bi_h}}{\beta' h'^2}\left(\frac{T_S}{T_B} - 1\right) = \eta\left(\frac{k_S}{k_B}\right)\left(\frac{C_{AS}}{C_{AB}}\right)^n$	(22)
$\beta = \beta'\left(\frac{T_B}{T_S}\right)\left(\frac{C_{AS}}{C_{AB}}\right)$	(24)
$\gamma = \gamma'\left(\frac{T_B}{T_S}\right)$	(27)
$\frac{k_S}{k_B} = \exp\left[-\gamma\left(1 - \frac{T_S}{T_B}\right)\right]$	(25)
$h = h'\left(\frac{k_S}{k_B}\right)^{1/2}\left(\frac{C_{AS}}{C_{AB}}\right)^{(n-1)/2}$	(21)
$\eta = \eta(n,h,\beta,\gamma)$	(15)
$\eta' = \eta\left(\frac{k_S}{k_B}\right)\left(\frac{C_{AS}}{C_{AB}}\right)^n$	(18)

In general, the relation expressed by Equation 15 will be in the form of a plot of numerical solutions to the intraparticle diffusion problem. The difficulties in applying such graphical results to iterative computerized design calculations might be avoided by use of the generalized Thiele modulus when applicable. Otherwise, it may be desirable to utilize approximate mathematical expressions for the effectiveness factor. For example:

$$\eta = \eta_{\text{iso}} + [\exp(\eta_{\text{iso}}) -][\exp(1.172\beta\sqrt{\gamma - 8}) - 1] \quad (29)$$

with

$$\eta_{\text{iso}} = \frac{3}{h_S}\left(\frac{1}{\tanh(h_S)} - \frac{1}{h_S}\right) \quad (30)$$

approximates the solutions of Weisz and Hicks (Module E3.3, Figure 1) for first-order reaction in the range $h_S > 2$, $\gamma > 8$(4). Approximate equations are also available for use with single site Langmuir-Hinshelwood and general order kinetics expressions(5).

DIAGNOSTIC CRITERIA

Very often in laboratory or pilot plant work, one is faced with the problem of simply identifying the important resistances, both heat and mass transfer, that must be considered in an analysis of results. A number of convenient "diagnostic criteria" are available for this purpose. First, consider the maximum temperature rise inside a catalyst particle. An upper bound can be calculated from Equation 6 of Module E3.3 in the absence of external heat and mass transfer resistances. Lee and Luss(6) have shown that Equation 31 provides an upper bound on the catalyst particle temperature when external resistances are significant:

$$\frac{T_{\text{Max}} - T_B}{T_B} = \beta'\left[1 + \Phi\left(\frac{1}{N_{Bi_h}} - \frac{1}{N_{Bi_m}}\right)\right] \quad (31)$$

where Φ is the observable Thiele modulus.

Several useful criteria are available for identifying regions where the absence of significant transport resistances is assured. Hudgins(7), using a pertubation technique, presented a criterion for avoiding intraparticle diffusion effects in an isothermal catalyst particle. Spherical particle geometry is assumed. His criterion is general in the sense that it may be applied to any rate expression of the form $R = R(C_A)$. In order to insure that the deviation of the observed reaction rate from the gradient-free rate be less than five percent, the inequality of Equation 32 must be satisfied.

$$\frac{R_{\text{obs}} r_o^2 |R'(C_{AS})|}{D_A^e R(C_{AS})} < 0.75 \quad (32)$$

Here, $R'(C_{AS})$ is the derivative of the rate expression with respect to C_A evaluated at the particle surface. Hudgins also developed a similar criterion to insure the absence of significant external mass transfer resistances(8):

$$\frac{R_{\text{obs}} r_o |R'(C_{AB})|}{k_c R(C_{AB})} < 0.15 \quad (33)$$

Analogous criteria for the absence of significant temperature gradients were derived by Anderson(9) for intraparticle heat transport and by Mears(10) for external heat transport. Anderson's criterion insures that the observed reaction rate not deviate by more than five percent from the rate in an isothermal particle:

$$\frac{R_{obs} r_o^2 |\Delta H_r| E_a}{\lambda^e R T_S^2} < 0.75 \tag{34}$$

Mear's criterion for negligible external heat transfer resistance is:

$$\frac{R_{obs} r_o |\Delta H_r| E_a}{h_c R T_B^2} < 0.15 \tag{35}$$

These equations are very convenient as a quick means of estimating which heat and mass transfer effects are important. Note, however, that their applicability is somewhat limited by the fact that the mass transfer criteria assume uniform temperature and the heat transfer criteria assume negligible gradients in concentration.

A frequently quoted rule of thumb is that while external mass transfer resistances can usually be neglected, intraparticle mass transfer resistances are often important. The opposite situation applies to heat transport—while intraparticle heat transfer resistances can frequently be neglected, external heat transfer resistances are often important. This second statement is usually applied in connection with the flow of gases past the particle at low Reynolds numbers.

If intraparticle diffusion significantly affects the reaction rate before external mass transfer resistance becomes significant then the criteria of Equations 32 and 33 require that:

$$N_{Sh}\left(\frac{D_A}{D_A^e}\right) > 10 \tag{36}$$

where $N_{Sh} = d_p k_c / D_A$ is the dimensionless Sherwood number. Similarly, if intraparticle heat transfer significantly affects the reaction rate in the absence of external heat transfer resistances, then it follows from Equations 34 and 35 that:

$$N_{Nu}\left(\frac{\lambda}{\lambda^e}\right) > 10 \tag{37}$$

and $N_{Nu} = d_p h_c / \lambda$ is the Nusselt number. Now the effective diffusivity, because of the reduced area and tortuous path that the diffusing molecules must experience, is always less than the bulk diffusivity. Usually the diffusivity ratio will fall in the range $3 < D_A/D_A^e < 16$. The opposite situation exists with respect to the effective thermal conductivity ratio in gas-filled pores. The thermal conductivity of the fluid is generally lower than that of the porous solid and typically $0.1 < \lambda/\lambda^e < 1.0$. For a spherical particle located in a stagnant fluid, it is easily shown that both N_{Sh} and N_{Nu} must equal two. At the low Reynolds numbers typical of laboratory reactors this may be taken as a practical lower limit. One concludes then that for gas phase flow in laboratory packed bed reactors, the inequality of Equation 36 is likely to be met, but the condition of Equation 37 will likely not hold. This result is consistent with previous statements. At the higher Reynolds numbers characteristic of many industrial reactors, both N_{Sh} and N_{Nu} exceed their minimum values and the inequality of Equation 37 may hold. Also, when the fluid phase is a liquid the ratio λ/λ^e will be closer to unity and Equation 37 might hold in some laboratory reactors.

COMMENTS ON MULTIPLICITY OF SOLUTIONS

Figure 1 of Module E3.3 presented an example of multiple steady-state solutions to the equations for intraparticle heat and mass transfer in porous catalysts. Three solutions were observed in this example, but it is theoretically possible to observe many more. Copelowitz and Aris found fifteen multiple solutions in numerical computations of first-order reaction in a sphere with $\beta = 2.5$ and $\gamma = 60$(11). Recently, Villadsen and Ivanov have shown that an infinite number of solutions is possible in spheres as $\beta \to \infty$(12). They've also shown that no more than three steady states can exist in cylinders and flat plates. These results are of interest primarily to theoreticians, as the parameter values are unrealistic. The practical upper limit on the adiabatic temperature rise, β, is about unity(13).

In the previous section it was found that the external heat transfer resistance would likely be of more importance than the intraparticle resistance for gas phase reactions. In many cases of practical importance it is reasonable to assume that the pellet is isothermal, but at a temperature different from the bulk fluid temperature. This does not eliminate the possibility of multiple steady states, however, since multiple solutions can arise as a consequence of finite external heat transfer resistances alone(14).

It is very easy to obtain a physical rational for up to three steady-state solutions to the equations describing diffusion and exothermic reaction within a catalyst particle. The *heat generation* rate is a sigmoidal function of temperature, beginning with an exponential rise due to the Arrhenius dependence of the rate constant, going through an inflection and then leveling off or decreasing as reactant is expended or chemical equilibrium is approached. The rate of *heat removal*, on the other hand, is roughly proportional to temperature, since the mechanism of heat transfer is either conduction (intraparticle) or convection (interparticle). At steady state, the heat generation and heat removal curves may intersect at as many as three points. Using similar arguments it can be shown that the combined effect of intra- and interparticle heat transfer resistances can result in up to five multiple steady-states.

Finally it is to be noted that multiplicities are possible in isothermal systems. Carberry discusses such an example in which the reaction kinetics is described by a dual site Langmuir-Hinshelwood mechanism(15). Thus the rate goes through a maximum when plotted against reactant concentration. The rate of external mass transport is proportional to reactant concentration. The intersections of the two curves define three steady states.

NOMENCLATURE

C = Concentration, gmol/cc.
C^* = Dimensionless concentration = C_A/C_{AS}.
D^e = Effective diffusivity, cm²/s.
d_p = Particle diameter, cm.
h = Thiele modulus.
h_c = Convective heat transfer coefficient, cal/cm²·s·K
k = Rate constant.
k_c = Convective mass transfer coefficient cm/s.
N = Molar flux, gmol/cm²·s.
N_{Bi_h} = Biot number for heat transfer. Equation 8.
N_{Bi_m} = Biot number for mass transfer, Equation 7.
N_{Nu} = Nusselt number = $d_p h_c/\lambda$
N_{Sh} = Sherwood number = $d_p k_c/D_A$
n = Reaction order.
q = Heat flux, cal/cm²·s.
R = Gas constant.
r = Length coordinate, spherical particle model, cm.
R = Reaction rate, gmol/cc·s.
R_{AW} = Molar rate of formation of component A, gmol/g·s.
T = Temperature, K.
x = Length coordinate, flat plate model, cm.
x^* = Dimensionless length coordinate, flat plate model = x/x_o.

Greek Letters:

β = Adiabatic temperature rise.
γ = Arrhenius number.
ΔH_r = Heat of reaction, cal/gmol.
η = Effectiveness factor.
λ^e = Effective thermal conductivity, cal/cm·s·K.
ρ_p = Particle density, g/cc.
Φ = Observable Thiele modulus.

Subscripts:

A = Component A.
B = Bulk fluid quantity.
obs = Observed quantity.
S = Surface quantity.

Note: All primed quantities are based upon bulk fluid properties.

LITERATURE CITED

1. Gillespie, B. M., E. D. Crandall and J. J. Carberry, *AIChE J.* 14, 483 (1968).
2. Aris, R., "The Mathematical Theory of Diffusion and Reaction in Permeable Catalysts. I. The Theory of The Steady State," Oxford University Press, London (1975).
3. Hlavacek, V. and M. Kubicek, *Chem. Eng. Sci.* 25, 1527 (1970).
4. Rajadhyaksha, R. A. and K. Vasudeva, *J. Catal.* 34, 321 (1974).
5. Rajadhyaksha, R. A., K. Vasudeva, and L. K. Doraiswamy, *J. Catal.* 41, 61 (1976).
6. Lee, J. C. M. and D. Luss, *Ind. Eng. Chem., Fund.* 8, 596 (1969).
7. Hudgins, R. R., *Chem. Eng. Sci.* 23, 93 (1968).
8. Hudgins, R. R., *Can. J. Chem. Eng.* 50, 427 (1972).
9. Anderson, J. B., *Chem. Eng. Sci.* 18, 147 (1963).
10. Mears, D. E., *J. Catal.* 20, 127 (1971).
11. Copelwitz, I. and R. Aris, *Chem. Eng. Sci.* 25, 906 (1970).
12. Villadsen, J. and E. Ivanov, *Chem. Eng. Sci.* 33, 41 (1978).
13. Weisz, P. B. and J. J. Hicks, *Chem. Eng. Sci.* 17, 264 (1962).
14. McGreavy, C. and J. M. Thornton, *Can. J. Chem. Eng.* 48, 187 (1970).
15. Carberry, J. J., "Chemical and Catalytic Reaction Engineering," McGraw-Hill, New York (1976).

STUDY PROBLEMS

1. Define and contrast η and η'. Explain the utility of each.

2. Can intraparticle mass transfer ever control the reaction? Can interparticle mass transfer ever control the reaction? Explain.

3. Discuss the physical significance of the heat and mass transfer Biot numbers.

4. Consider the summary of equations in Table 1. What quantities are known in a typical design problem? What quantities are unknown? Outline a method for solving these questions.

5. When solving problems involving intraparticle heat and mass transfer in porous catalysts we have a choice of two sets of boundary conditions at the surface: 1) Equations 5 and 6 or 2) Equations 13 and 14. Under what circumstances will the two give identical results?

HOMEWORK PROBLEMS

1. Show how the equations in Table 1 can be reduced to Equation 28 for an isothermal first-order reaction.

2. Solve Equation 9 for first-order reaction in a slab using the boundary conditions, Equations 5 and 11, and evaluate the effectiveness factor. Compare your result with Equation 28.

3. Obtain an equation analogous to Equation 28 for spherical particle geometry.

4. The reaction $A \to B$ takes place in the gas phase in a plug flow reactor charged with 7.0 tons of catalyst. The reactor operates at atmospheric pressure and 500 K. The catalyst is in the form of spheres 0.32 cm in diameter. Catalyst particle density is 1.5 gm/cc. At 500 K the true kinetics can be described by the first-order expression, $-R_{AW} = kC_A$, where k = 500 cc/gm·s. The component A effective diffusivity and the external mass transfer coefficient are estimated to be 0.085 cm²/s and 6.0 cm/s respectively. Calculate the conversion if the feed consists of pure A flowing at a rate of 8×10^6 scf/h. Assume that the reactor is isothermal.

5. Derive a criterion for determining the relative significance of intraparticle heat and mass transfer resistances. Assume power law kinetics. Rank the various heat and mass transport resistances in order of decreasing importance for strongly exothermic reactions ($|\gamma\beta/n| > 1$). Repeat for moderately exothermic reactions ($|\gamma\beta/n| \cong 1$).

6. The reaction $A \to B$ takes place over a heterogeneous catalyst in a continuous flow, stirred tank

reactor. The reaction is elementary second-order in A. The concentration of reactant leaving the reactor is 0.10 gmol/L and the observed reaction rate is 0.30 gmol/g cat. h. The effective diffusivity is estimated to be 0.2 cm²/s. The spherical catalyst particle diameter is 6 mm and the particle density is 1.5 g/cc. The heat of reaction is approximately zero. Comment on the significance of intraparticle diffusion resistance.

Module E3.5

Heat and Mass Transfer in Packed Beds-I

H. W. Haynes, Jr.

Department of Chemical Engineering
University of Wyoming
Laramie, WY 82071

OBJECTIVES
After completing this module, the student should be able to:
1. Estimate bed and particle associated heat and mass transfer parameters in packed beds from published correlations.

PREREQUISITE MATHEMATICAL SKILLS
1. Elementary calculus through differential equations.

PREREQUISITE ENGINEERING AND SCIENCE SKILLS
1. Stimulus-response techniques as applied to chemical reactors.
2. Transport phenomena—analogies between heat and mass transfer; radiation, convection, conduction.

This module will be concerned with correlations of bed and particle associated heat and mass transfer parameters in packed beds. The bed parameters include the axial and radial dispersion coefficients, D_z and D_r, the analogous effective bed thermal conductivities, λ_z and λ_r, and the wall heat transfer coefficient, h_w. Since fluid flows in the axial direction only, it is necessary to make this distinction between axial and radial parameter values. It will be assumed throughout the discussion that the bed velocity is radially uniform and that the bed transport parameters are independent of position in the bed. These assumptions are quite reasonable in large diameter beds, but modifications to the model described here may be necessary if the engineer is confronted with a bed for which $d_t/d_p < 30$ [1,2,3]. The particle associated parameters of interest are the convective external heat and mass transfer coefficients, h_c and k_c, which were employed in Module E3.4.

BED MASS TRANSFER PARAMETERS

The dispersion of mass in packed beds is normally described in terms of Fickian dispersion coefficients as defined in Equations 1 and 2:

$$N_z = -D_z \frac{\partial C}{\partial z} \qquad (1)$$

$$N_r = -D_r \frac{\partial C}{\partial r} \qquad (2)$$

The fluxes are defined on the basis of a cross-section of bed area*. It is important to recognize that one is concerned here with mass transfer external to the catalyst particles, i.e. the mass transfer due to mixing and molecular diffusion within and among the voids between particles. Consequently, experiments aimed at the characterization of dispersion in packed beds are most conveniently conducted on beds of nonporous particles.

Axial Dispersion Coefficient, D_z:

The experimental evaluation of the axial dispersion coefficient consists of subjecting the bed to a time-varying stimulus of inert tracer at or near the inlet and recording the response at or near the outlet. Typical forcing functions include sinusoidal, step, impulse, and one-shot arbitrary (pulse) inputs. For certain simplified boundary conditions, the unsteady-state tracer mass balance (linear PDE) can be solved analytically [4,5] and D_z can be obtained by a regression on the response curve in the time domain. Alternatively, D_z can be obtained in the absence of a time-domain solution by techniques commonly employed in the analysis of stimulus-response data comparison of moments [6], Fourier transform analysis [7], etc. For more general boundary conditions which take into account differing degrees of dispersion in the fore and aft zones of the bed, no analytical solution has been obtained. Van der Laan derived the first and second moments of the residence time distribution curve for a number of configurations [8]. For small deviations from plug flow, the result is independent of "end effects" and the choice of boundary conditions becomes unimportant.

---
* Some authors base their definitions on a cross-section of bed *void* area, and the resulting dispersion coefficients must be multiplied by a factor ϵ, the bed porosity, for equivalence with these definitions.

Axial dispersion coefficients have been measured in numerous laboratories by a variety of these techniques and excellent summaries are available(9,10). The results are usually presented in the form of a dimensionless plot for the particle Peclet number, $N_{Pe_{m,z,p}} = ud_p/D_z$ [The cumbersome subscripts, implying mass transfer (m) in the axial direction (z), with characteristic length $d_p(p)$, are necessary to avoid confusion with other Peclet numbers to be encountered later]. For gases, $N_{Pe_{m,z,p}}$ is observed to increase linearly with particle Reynolds number, go through a slight maximum, and then remain constant at a value of about 2.0 for $N_{Re_p} > 10$ approximately. A different behavior is observed with liquids. In this case $N_{Pe_{m,z,p}}$ remains constant at a value of about 0.4 over a wide range of Reynolds numbers below about 10. A gradual increase in $N_{Pe_{m,z,p}}$ is observed with increase in N_{Re_p} greater than 10 until ultimately a value of about 2 is attained. Data from the literature are summarized in Figures 1 and 2, taken from the text by Wen and Fan(10).

Dimensional analysis considerations require that the particle Peclet number be correlated with the Reynolds number *and* the molecular Schmidt number, N_{Sc}. Considering that N_{Sc_f} for gases is of the order of unity, and N_{Sc_f} for liquids is of the order of 10^3, it is not surprising that different curves are required for gases and liquids when the data are plotted according to either of the Figures 1 or 2.

The two curves do have one feature in common, however. The Peclet number approaches an asymptotic value of about 2 at high Reynolds numbers. (Note that the ordinate of Figure 2 is $\epsilon N_{Pe_{m,z,p}}$, and that ϵ for packed beds is normally in the range $0.35 < \epsilon < 0.5$). Thus from experiment it is concluded that $N_{Pe_{m,z,p}} \cong 2$ in the turbulent flow regime, or:

$$D_z = \frac{1}{2} u d_p \quad \text{(turbulent flow, gases and liquids)} \tag{3}$$

and indeed a simple model of turbulent mixing on the scale of one particle diameter predicts just such a result (See Homework Problem 1).

In the opposite extreme, i.e. at very low flow rates, one would expect the axial dispersion of gases to be dominated by a molecular diffusion process. Thus:

$$D_z = \frac{\epsilon}{\tau} D_m \quad \text{(laminar flow, gases)} \tag{4}$$

where τ is a bed tortuosity factor accounting for deviousness of path and the factor ϵ is needed to account for the reduction in cross-sectional area available for diffusion. To a good first approximation, the transition between these two extremes can be described by the additive formula:

$$D_z = \frac{\epsilon}{\tau} D_m + \frac{1}{2} u d_p \quad \text{(gases)} \tag{5}$$

or, in terms of dimensionless quantities,

$$\frac{1}{N_{Pe_{m,z,p}}} = \frac{\epsilon}{\tau N_{Re_p} N_{Sc_f}} + \frac{1}{2} \quad \text{(gases)} \tag{6}$$

This equation does not predict the hump in Figure 1

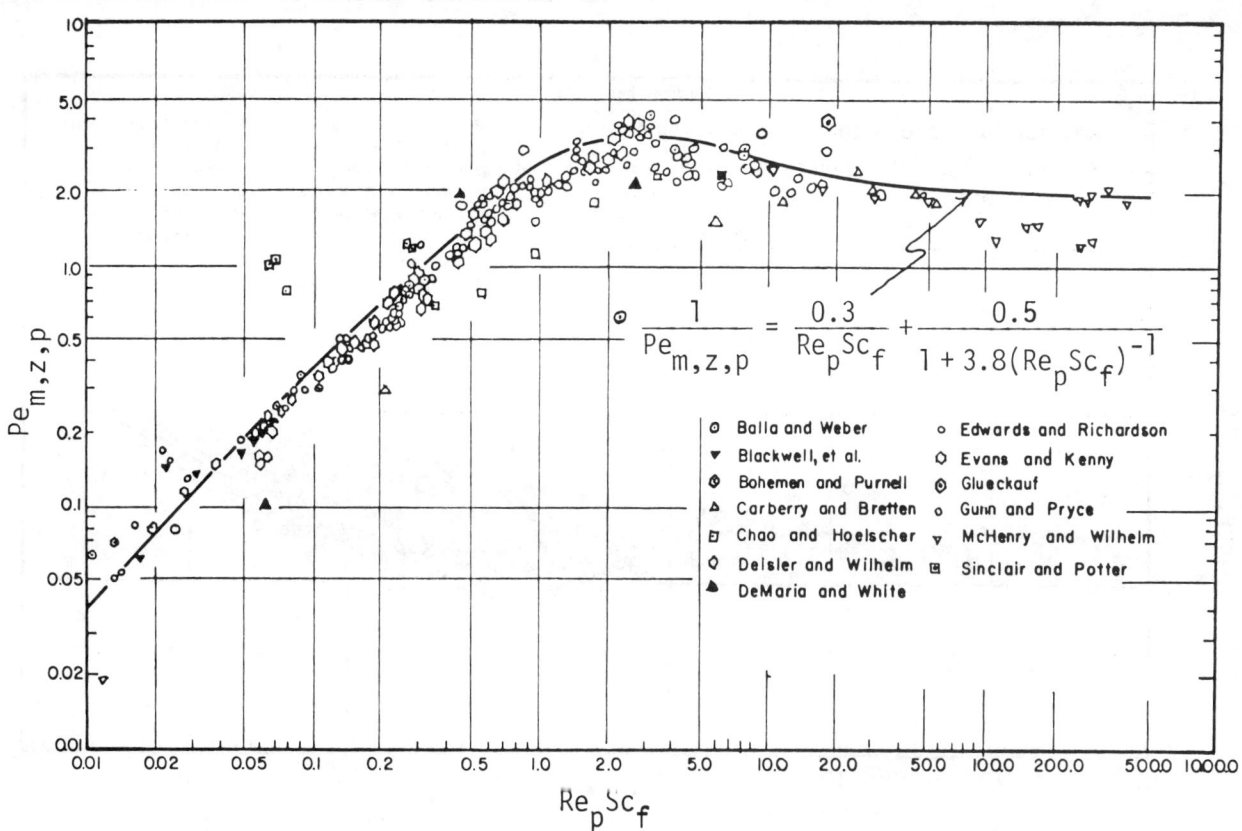

Figure 1. Correlation of the axial dispersion coefficient for gases in packed beds(10).

and consequently, an empirical modification is sometimes employed. One such modification is an equation of the form(11):

$$\frac{1}{N_{Pe_{m,z,p}}} = \frac{\varepsilon}{\tau N_{Re_p} N_{Sc_f}} + \frac{0.5}{1 + \beta(N_{Re_p} N_{Sc_f})^{-1}} \quad \text{(gases)} \quad (7)$$

which has been plotted in Figure 1.

The molecular diffusivities for liquids are some four or five orders of magnitude smaller than gas phase diffusivities. Molecular diffusion would not be expected, therefore, to contribute significantly to dispersion in liquids even in the laminar flow region; and indeed studies at very low Reynolds numbers have failed to identify a dependence similar to Equation 4 (See Figure 2). Gunn(12) and others(13) have developed a model of dispersion in packed beds which puts these observations for gases and liquids on a common theoretical basis. On a scale of about one particle diameter, the fluid consists of fast-flowing regions and relatively slow (stagnant according to the model) regions, with interchange by molecular diffusion between the two. Axial dispersion by molecular diffusion is included in the mass balances for both the stagnant and flowing streams. Gunn's model provides a correlation of the form:

$$\frac{1}{N_{Pe_{m,z,p}}} = \frac{\varepsilon}{N_{Re_p} N_{Sc_f}} + \left(\frac{1-p}{2p}\right)\left(\frac{1}{x}\right) \times \left\{1 - \frac{1}{2x}(1 - e^{-2x})\right\} \quad (8)$$

where

$$x = \frac{11.566(1 - \varepsilon)}{p(1 - p)N_{Re_p} N_{Sc_f}} \quad (9)$$

and p is the probability that a randomly selected fluid element is located in the flowing stream. Using liquid phase dispersion data (and thereby avoiding complications from molecular diffusion) Gunn empirically related this probability to the Reynolds number and the results are provided in Table 1. Equation 8 appears to correlate all the available axial dispersion data, both gas and liquid phase, in packed beds provided that natural convection is absent(13).

Radial Dispersion Coefficient, D_r:

Measurements of the radial dispersion coefficient are conducted in a steady-state experiment in which an inert tracer is injected continuously within and on the centerline of the bed and sampling is conducted on a

Table 1. Probability, p, as a function of Reynolds number(12).

N_{Re_p}	p
1	0.17
4	0.18
10	0.20
20	0.275
40	0.36
100	0.43
200	0.47
400	0.48
1000	0.59

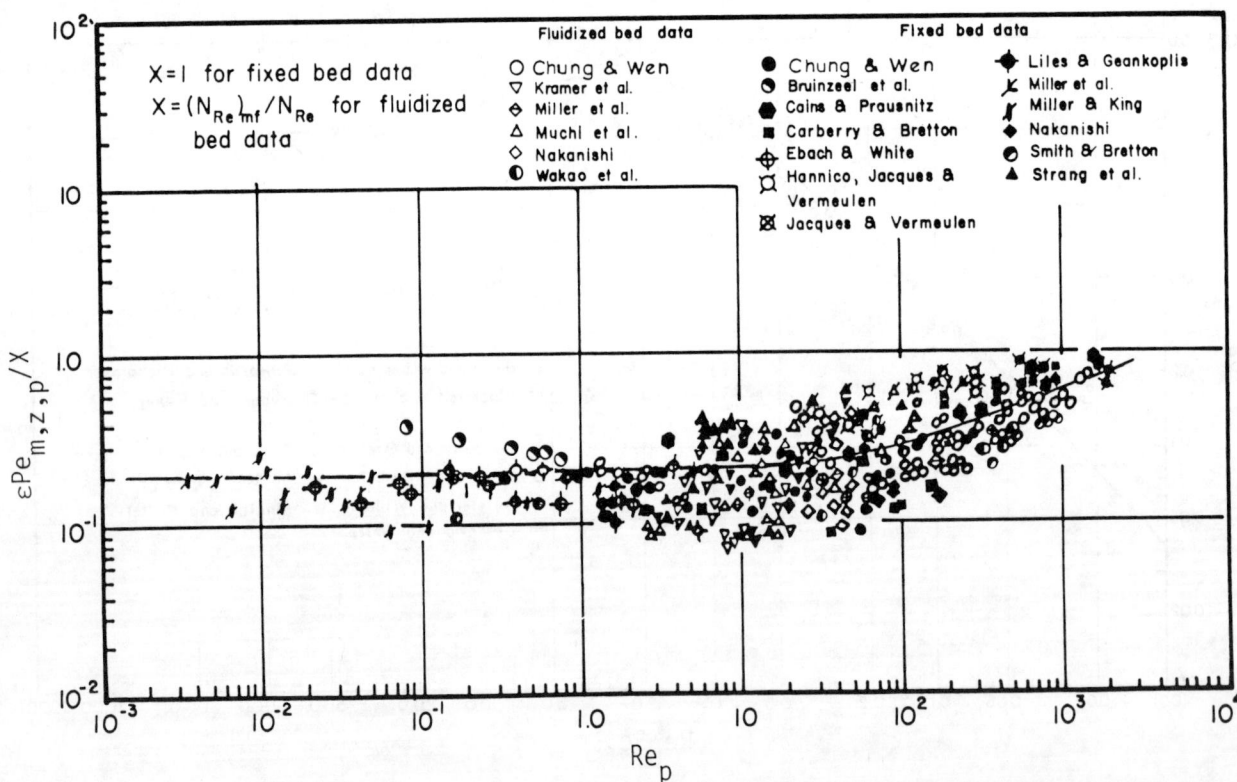

Figure 2. Correlation of the axial dispersion coefficient for liquids in packed beds(10).

downstream cross-section at different radial positions. The differential mass balance equations have been solved for a general model which includes finite injection source, arbitrary axial dispersion contribution, finite tube diameter, and boundary conditions at the inlet and outlet which allow for dispersion in the fore and aft zones of the reactor(*14*). Most investigators, however, have used some simplification of the general solution for data analysis purposes. Often these simplifications can be justified. From a comparison of the general solution with various simplifications, Levenspiel and Bischoff concluded that the common assumption of a point source is justifiable provided that the ratio of the injection tube diameter to the bed diameter is less than 0.2(*14*). They also concluded that end effects are smaller than with axial dispersion measurements. Neglecting the axial dispersion term in the analysis can lead to significant errors in the computed value of D_r(*15*). Only when the dispersion mechanism is primarily one of molecular diffusion is it permissible to assume for simplification purposes that the axial dispersion and radial dispersion coefficients are equal. Studies in which the axial dispersion coefficient has been neglected, or set equal to the radial dispersion coefficient should therefore be viewed with suspicion.

Correlations for the radial dispersion coefficient in packed beds are presented in Figures 3 and 4(*10*). As was observed with the axial dispersion data, the liquid phase and gas phase radial dispersion data fall on different curves when the Peclet number is plotted versus either N_{Re_p} or $N_{Re_p} N_{Sc_f}$. At high Reynolds numbers in the turbulent flow region, both sets of data are convergent to a common Peclet number, $N_{Pe_{m,r,p}} \cong 11$. Ranz computed a theoretical value of 11.2 using a model which assumes a simple lateral displacement of fluid at each encounter with a bed particle(*16*). At low flow rates the mechanism of radial dispersion for gases is one of molecular diffusion and Equation 4 can be used to calculate the radial dispersion coefficient. Gunn recommends summing the diffusive and connective Peclet numbers as follows(*12*):

$$\frac{1}{N_{Pe_{m,r,p}}} = \frac{\varepsilon}{\tau N_{Re_p} N_{Sc_f}} + \frac{1}{N_{Pe_c}} \qquad (10)$$

The convective Peclet number was calculated from liquid-phase radial dispersion data and tabulated as a function of Reynolds number (Table 2). Equation 10 is a general correlation for the radial dispersion coefficient which can be applied to both liquid and gas phase systems.

Table 2. Dependence of convective radial Peclet number upon Reynolds number(*12*).

N_{Re_p}	N_{Pe_c}
< 1	40
5	32
10	25
20	22
40	18
100	14
200	12
400	11
1000	11

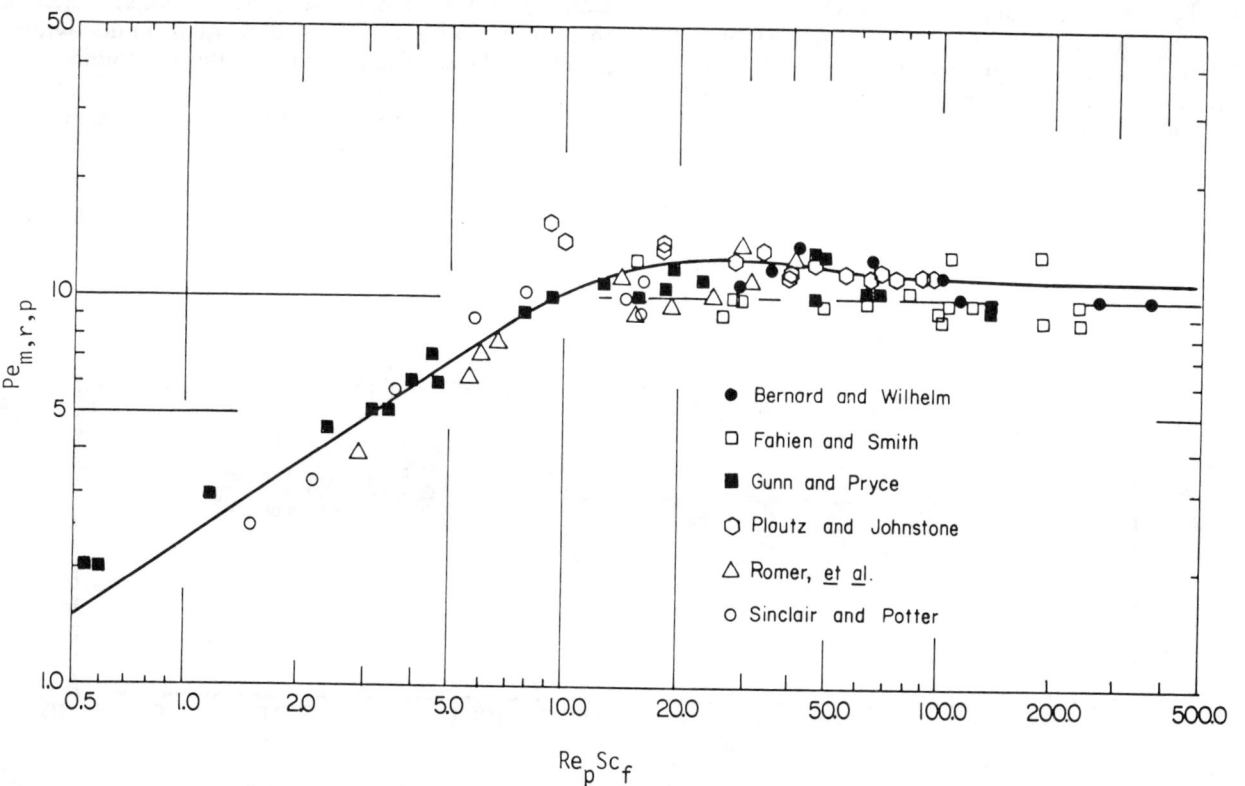

Figure 3. Correlation of the radial dispersion coefficient for gases in packed beds(*10*).

BED HEAT TRANSFER PARAMETERS

Recall from previous courses in transport phenomena that certain analogies exist between heat and mass transfer at low mass transfer rates. A heat transfer correlation can be obtained from a mass transfer correlation (and vice-versa) by interchange of the groups Sc and Pr, Sh and Nu, etc. The Peclet number for radial transfer can be written:

$$N_{Pe_{m,r,p}} = \frac{d_p u}{D_r} = \left(\frac{d_p u \rho}{\mu}\right)\left(\frac{\mu}{\rho D_r}\right) = N_{Re_p} N_{Sc_r} \quad (11)$$

Therefore, one employs an analogous Peclet number for radial heat transfer, which is written as:

$$N_{Pe_{h,r,p}} = N_{Re_p} N_{Pr_r} = \left(\frac{d_p u \rho}{\mu}\right)\left(\frac{C_p \mu}{\lambda_r}\right) = \frac{d_p u \rho C_p}{\lambda_r} \quad (12)$$

where λ_r is the effective bed thermal conductivity in the radial direction. The axial heat transfer Peclet number is written in exactly the same fashion. The defining equation for the bed thermal conductivity is, of course, Fourier's law of heat conduction. In the radial direction one has:

$$q_r = -\lambda_r \frac{\partial T}{\partial r} \quad (13)$$

and in the axial direction:

$$q_z = -\lambda_z \frac{\partial T}{\partial z} \quad (14)$$

Since correlations have been developed for the mass transfer Peclet number in terms of the particle Reynolds and the molecular Schmidt numbers, one may attempt to use these same correlations (with the molecular Prandtl number replacing the Schmidt number) for calculating the heat transfer Peclet numbers. Unfortunately, the situation is a great deal more complicated than is indicated by this approach. Rates of heat transfer are also influenced by such factors as conduction through the solid particles and radiation between particles which have no mass transfer analogy. In order to take these additional factors into account, it is necessary to postulate a model of the heat transfer process.

In addition to the thermal conductivities, heat transfer at the wall must be considered in order to provide a complete description of bed heat transfer. In many of the earlier studies especially, radial conduction through the bed and conduction at the wall were lumped into a single overall heat transfer coefficient. A number of correlations for this overall heat transfer coefficient are available, the most notable of which is perhaps due to Leva(17). More recent authors have separated these two factors and analyzed their results in terms of an actual or true wall heat transfer coefficient. In this case, the local wall heat transfer coefficient is defined according to:

$$q_r = h_w(T - T_w) \quad (15)$$

Radial Thermal Conductivity, λ_r:

The experimental set-up for measuring radial thermal conductivity usually involves the steady-state heating or cooling of a fluid flowing through the bed by means of a jacket surrounding the wall of the vessel. Thermocouples are installed within the bed or in the outlet stream. The parameter values are obtained by comparing the solution to the differential energy balance equation with the experimental temperatures. An analytical solution is available for the energy balance equation which includes both radial and axial thermal conductivities as well as wall heat transfer(18). However, most investigators have chosen to simplify their analysis by eliminating the axial thermal conductivity term from the equations. Gros and Bugarel found their computations to be insensitive to the axial thermal conductivity over the range of Reynolds numbers

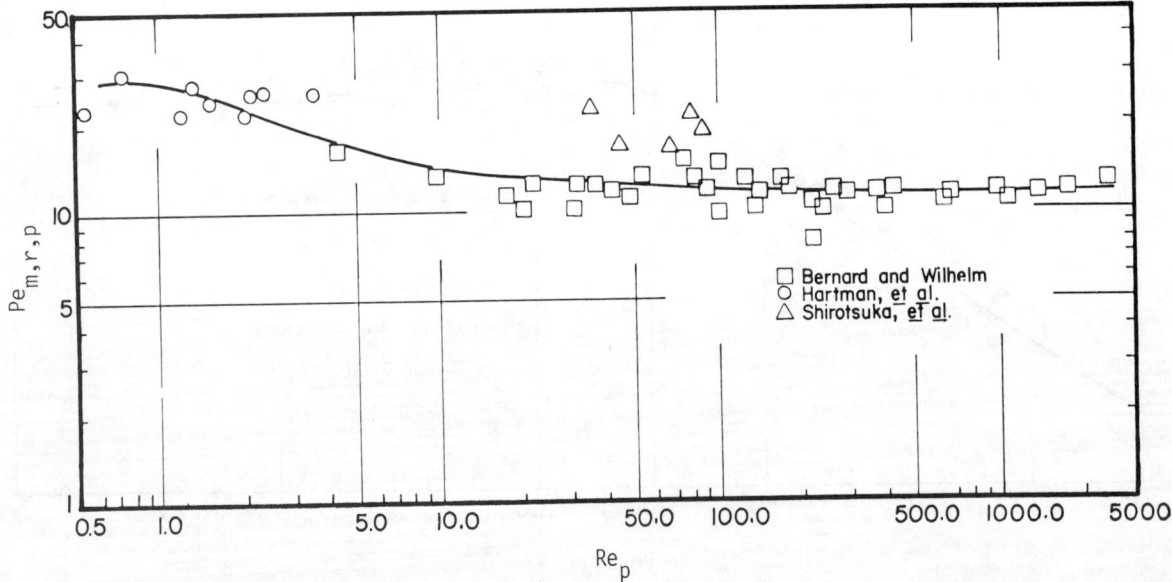

Figure 4. Correlation of the radial dispersion coefficient for liquids in packed beds(10).

studied (40–500); thus supporting this common simplification for the analysis of experiments at high Reynolds numbers(*19*).

As pointed out earlier, radial heat transfer due to the lateral displacement of fluid is only one of several mechanisms which must be considered in characterizing heat transfer in packed beds. Several models have been proposed for correlating radial thermal conductivities (e.g. *20,21,22*). One of the first and indeed one of the more successful, is the model due to Yagi and Kunii(*21*). These authors considered the following heat transfer mechanisms *independent* of fluid flow:

1. Thermal conduction through solid.
2. Thermal conduction at point contacts.
3. Radiant heat transfer between particles (gases only).
4. Radiant heat transfer between voids (gases only).

In addition are the following heat transfer mechanisms *dependent* upon fluid flow:

5. Thermal conduction through fluid near point contacts.
6. Convective heat transfer between solids and fluid.
7. Heat transfer by lateral mixing of fluid.

The mechanisms are illustrated by number in Figure 5. Yagi and Kunii argued that because the contact surfaces between particles are normally embedded in boundary layers, mechanism 5 could be taken as independent of fluid flow. Furthermore, they neglected mechanism 6 entirely, by virtue of its small influence in comparison to the other modes of heat transfer. And finally, upon comparison of their model with experimental data it was found that the conduction between point contacts, mechanism 2, was also of negligible importance.

With these simplifications in effect, the only heat transfer mechanism dependent upon fluid flow is the lateral mixing term, mechanism 7. Yagi and Kunii employed an equation from Ranz's lateral dispersion model(*16*) to compute this term; however, equivalent results can be obtained from the following considerations*. From Figures 3 and 4 it is apparent that for $N_{Re_p} \geq 10$, the mass transfer Peclet number is the same for gases and liquids and therefore independent of the molecular Schmidt number. Thus $N_{Pe_{m,r,p}}$ is a function of the Reynolds number only, and it follows from the analogy between heat and mass transfer that $N_{Pe_{h,r,p}}$ (mixing or flow contribution only) must be this same function of Reynolds number, i.e.,

$$N_{Pe_{h,r,p}}(\text{flow}) \cong N_{Pe_{m,r,p}} = 11 \qquad (16)$$

Substituting from Equation 12 gives for the flow or lateral mixing contribution to the effective radial thermal conductivity,

$$\lambda_r^f = \alpha d_p u \rho C_p \qquad (17)$$

where $\alpha = 1/N_{Pe_{m,r,p}} \cong 0.091$ is Ranz's lateral displacement factor.

---
*This is actually a "streamlined" version of the original model. The length parameters, γ and β, in the original model are taken as unity in practical applications and will be presented as such here.

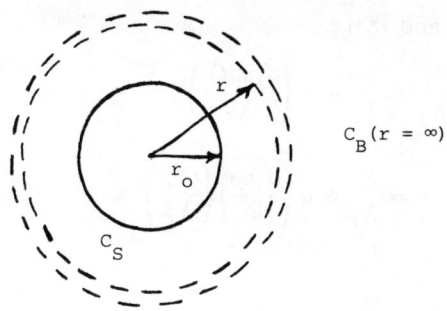

Figure 5. Yagi and Kunii model of heat transfer in packed beds(*21*).

Now consider the thermal conductivity caused by mechanisms 1,3,4 and 5 which are independent (approximately, in the case of mechanism 5) of fluid flow. For motionless fluids Yagi and Kunii obtained:

$$\lambda_r^o = \frac{1-\varepsilon}{\dfrac{1}{\lambda_s} + \dfrac{1}{\lambda_f/\psi + d_p h_{rs}}} + \varepsilon d_p h_{rv} \qquad (18)$$

where λ_s and λ_f are the thermal conductivities of the solid and fluid phases respectively, ψ is the effective thickness of the fluid film at the point contacts/particle diameter (mechanism 5) and h_{rs} and h_{rv} are the solid-solid and void-void radiation terms respectively. The radiation heat transfer coefficients are given by:

$$h_{rs} = 4\sigma \left(\frac{e}{2-e}\right) T^3 \qquad (19)$$

and

$$h_{rv} = \frac{4\sigma T^3}{1 + \dfrac{\varepsilon}{2(1-\varepsilon)}\left(\dfrac{1-e}{e}\right)} \qquad (20)$$

The parameter ψ was obtained from a comparison of Equation 18 with experimental thermal conductivities in beds of motionless fluids. It was found that this parameter could be correlated with void fraction and fluid thermal conductivity as follows (the equations are equivalent to Figures 9 and 10 of Reference 21):

$$\ln \psi_{\text{air}} = 1.810 \ln \varepsilon - 1.714 \qquad (21)$$

and

$$\frac{\psi}{\psi_{\text{air}}} = \left(\frac{\lambda_f}{\lambda_{\text{air}}}\right)^{0.36} \qquad (22)$$

The small magnitude of ψ indicates that the thickness of the fluid conduction path is small in comparison to the particle diameter and Yagi and Kunii cite this result as supporting their claim that mechanism 5 is independent of flow.

Under the stated assumptions, the thermal conductivity for the motionless fluid remains constant as flow is varied. Thus, the effective thermal conductivity can be obtained by summing the contributions, Equations

17 and 18, i.e.,

$$\frac{\lambda_r}{\lambda_f} = \frac{\lambda_r^o}{\lambda_f} + \alpha \left(\frac{d_p u \rho C_p}{\lambda_f} \right)$$

$$= \frac{\lambda_r^o}{\lambda_f} + \alpha \left(\frac{d_p u \rho}{\mu} \right) \left(\frac{C_p \mu}{\lambda_f} \right)$$

or

$$\frac{\lambda_r}{\lambda_f} = \frac{\lambda_r^o}{\lambda_f} + \alpha N_{Re_p} N_{Pr_f} \qquad (23)$$

Equation 23 predicts that a plot of reduced radial thermal conductivity versus Reynolds number will be a straight line for a given fluid. Experimental plots are consistent with this equation; the parameter α does, however, differ somewhat from the value expected from radial mass transfer results. Yagi and Kunii found that for spheres, cylinders and broken granules, the values of α cover a range from about 0.1 to 0.14.

Space does not permit a summary of other models for calculating radial effective thermal conductivities in packed beds. A model due to Argo and Smith is discussed in the text by Smith(23). The model includes terms to account for fluid conduction, convective dispersion, radiation and solid conduction. The convective dispersion term is identical to the corresponding term (mechanism 7) in the Yagi and Kunii model. The radiation term is of similar form, but generally smaller than the Yagi and Kunii term (mechanism 4). No fluid conduction term is contained in the Yagi and Kunii model and this might be considered a deficiency, especially when the model is applied to liquid phase systems. The solid conduction terms are different in the two models. Most notably, Argo and Smith provide for velocity dependent convective heat transfer between the fluid and particle. The omission of this mode in the Yagi and Kunii model has been criticized(24). On the other hand, it is claimed that Argo and Smith's model predicts too great a sensitivity to high values of the solid conductivity at high Reynolds numbers(25).

It may be necessary to take into account the Smoluchowski effect when beds of small particles are operated at low pressures(22,26). When the mean free path of the gas phase molecules is of the same order as the distance between particles, the thermal conductivity is reduced. In a motionless bed most of the conduction takes place near the point contacts and the falling off of thermal conductivity can be significant even when the distance between particles is larger than the mean free path by a factor of 1000. According to Schotte, this effect is significant when the operating pressure is below the "break-away" pressure, which may be calculated from:

$$P_b = 4.26 \times 10^{-20} \frac{T}{d_p \sigma^2} \qquad (24)$$

with P_b in atm, T in K, and d_p and σ, both in cm.

Axial Thermal Conductivity, λ_z:

Measurements of the effective thermal conductivity in the axial direction are quite limited. The most detailed study appears to be that of Gunn and de Souza(27). These investigators heated air flowing into a packed column in such a fashion that a sinusoidal temperature wave was introduced into the bed. The temperature of the exiting air was recorded and from a frequency response analysis, the model parameters, i.e. the axial thermal conductivity and the convective fluid-particle heat transfer coefficient, were calculated (The bed was insulated in order to eliminate radial conductivity effects. Also, the particle thermal conductivity was a parameter in the model, but the experiment was insensitive to this quantity due to the rapidity of thermal conduction within the particles). It was observed that molecular conduction dominated the axial dispersion at $N_{Re_p} < 10$. For $N_{Re_p} > 10$ convection dispersion effects grew to dominance. Generally the heat transfer Peclet number, $N_{Pe_h,r,p}$, was smaller than the corresponding $N_{Pe_m,r,p}$, probably as a consequence of the solid conduction contribution to heat transfer (No temperatures were given, but presumably they were sufficiently low that radiation effects were not a factor.).

Several authors have evaluated axial bed thermal conductivities from the steady-state heated wall experiments described earlier in the discussion of radial thermal conductivity. Generally these experiments are not very sensitive to λ_z, but values so obtained are qualitatively in agreement with the measurements of Gunn and de Souza(18,19).

It appears that no attempts have been made to model axial conduction of heat in packed beds. Presumably this is because of the widespread practice of neglecting axial thermal conduction in the design of packed bed reactors (See Module E3.6). There seems to be no fundamental reason why the radial thermal conductivity models discussed in the previous section cannot be applied to the axial conduction problem, provided that the axial convection mass dispersion term is substituted for the corresponding radial term.

Wall Heat Transfer Coefficient, h_w:

In 1963 Beek (25) stated, "There is even more uncertainty in estimating the heat transfer coefficient at the wall of the tube than in estimating the effective thermal conductivity in the bed of catalyst." Unfortunately, the situation is no different today. Many correlations for the wall heat transfer coefficient have been proposed, but predicted values differ by as much as an order of magnitude. One reason for this is apparent from an analysis of the experimental technique commonly used to evaluate wall heat transfer coefficients. Most investigators have determined h_w in the same steady-state heating (or cooling) experiment used to evaluate λ_r (18,19,28,29). The differential energy balance equation for the packed bed is solved, taking into account wall heat transfer in the boundary conditions, and h_w is adjusted along with λ_r (and perhaps λ_z) in order to obtain the best fit, i.e. minimum error, between observed and calculated temperatures. Normally it is observed that the minimum error is not very sensitive to values of h_w(29), so that the experimental uncertainties in reported values of the wall heat transfer coefficient are large.

For $N_{Re_p} > 40$, Beck recommends the following empirical modification of the Thoenes-Kramers formula for application to beds packed with cylinders(25):

$$N_{Nuw} = 2.58\, N_{Re_p}^{0.333} N_{Pr_f}^{0.333}$$
$$+ 0.094\, N_{Re_p}^{0.8} N_{Pr_f}^{0.4} \quad \text{(cylinders)} \quad (25)$$

where $N_{Nuw} = h_w d_p/\lambda_f$ is the wall Nusselt number. For beds packed with spheres, the wall is less obstructed and heat transfer to the wall is more like that of an empty tube. A stronger dependence upon N_{Re_p} is therefore evident. For $N_{Re_p} > 40$:

$$N_{Nuw} = 0.203\, N_{Re_p}^{0.333} N_{Pr_f}^{0.333}$$
$$+ 0.220\, N_{Re_p}^{0.8} N_{Pr_f}^{0.4} \quad \text{(spheres)} \quad (26)$$

Yagi and Kunii(30) have proposed a correlation for the wall heat transfer coefficient which is identical in form to Equation 23. Thus:

$$N_{Nuw} = N_{Nuw}^o + \alpha_w N_{Re_p} N_{Pr_f} \quad (27)$$

The form of this equation was verified by experiments involving heat flow between walls in an annular packed bed. In contrast to the experiments that were described previously, the conductivity at the wall was determined by extrapolating the bed temperature profile to the wall and calculating h_w from the resulting ΔT and the measured flux. Data for spherical particles in cylindrical packed beds could be correlated with Equation 27 with $\alpha_w = 0.054$. The observation that α_w is about one half of α (Equation 23) suggests that lateral mixing near the wall is about half that in the bed. Values of the motionless fluid wall Nusselt group, N_{Nuw}^o, varied considerably over a range from about 1 to 8, thus limiting the predictive capabilities of the correlation.

PARTICLE ASSOCIATED TRANSPORT COEFFICIENTS

The operation of a heterogeneous catalytic reactor generally involves an interchange of mass and energy between the bulk fluid and the external surface of the catalyst particles. The influence of external heat and mass transfer on catalyst effectiveness was discussed in a previous module. Here, correlations are presented for the convective mass and heat transfer coefficients in packed beds. By definition:

$$N_A = k_c(C_{AS} - C_{AB}) \quad (28)$$

and

$$q = h_c(T_S - T_B) \quad (29)$$

where N_A is the molar flux of species A emitted from the catalyst particle and q is the heat flux. The S and B subscripted quantities are evaluated at the particle surface and in the bulk fluid respectively.

Studies on particle associated mass transfer in packed beds are numerous. Most investigators have evaluated mass transfer coefficients from the steady-state dissolution or evaporation of species from the particle surface into a flowing liquid or gas. The evaporation of adsorbed water and sublimation of naphthalene particles are common techniques in this class. Mass transfer coefficients can also be calculated from reaction kinetics experiments when rates are external mass transfer controlled; and heat transfer coefficients can be evaluated simultaneously from measured temperatures and a knowledge of the heat of reaction. Heat transfer coefficients can be calculated from steady-state experiments in which the bed particles are evenly heated. Microwave heating has been employed for this purpose. In principle, both mass and heat transfer coefficients can be determined by unsteady state (stimulus-response) techniques; however, because of the rapidity of the external mass transfer process and the large number of parameters affecting the results, it is difficult to evaluate k_c by unsteady-state methods. The evaluation of h_c by unsteady-state methods appears to have been more successful.

Experimental mass and heat transfer coefficients are often correlated in terms of the j factor. For mass transfer:

$$j_m = \frac{k_c}{u}\left(\frac{\mu}{\rho D_m}\right)^{2/3} = \frac{N_{Sh_p}}{N_{Re_p} N_{Sc_f}^{1/3}} \quad (30)$$

For heat transfer:

$$j_h = \frac{h_c}{u\rho C_p}\left(\frac{C_p \mu}{\lambda_f}\right)^{2/3} = \frac{N_{Nu_p}}{N_{Re_p} N_{Pr_f}^{1/3}} \quad (31)$$

Recently, Hsiung and Thodos(31) summarized the mass transfer results of a number of investigators in an equation of the form:

$$j_m = 1.33/N_{Re_p}^{0.4} \quad (32)$$

This equation is intended for use over the range $0.1 < N_{Re_p} < 100$. From the analogy between mass and heat transfer, one would expect that $j_m = j_h$. However, most investigators report a somewhat higher value of j_h. It is likely that the higher j_h values are due to contributions from thermal conduction and radiation. Using data for which these effects were thought to be a minimum, Sen Gupta and Thodos(32) found the ratio j_h/j_m to be approximately unity.

Equations 30 and 32 can be rearranged to obtain:

$$N_{Sh_p} = 1.33\, N_{Sc_f}^{1/3} N_{Re_p}^{0.6} \quad (33)$$

The form of this equation is inconsistent with the idea of a limiting value of the Sherwood number as the Reynolds number approaches zero. For mass transfer from an isolated sphere in a stagnant fluid it can be shown that $N_{Sh_p} = 2$ (See Homework Problem 5). Indeed, correlations for N_{Sh_p}, or equivalently N_{Nu_p}, in packed beds as summarized by Kunii and Suzuki(33) reveal that values of these groups as small as 10^{-4} have been reported. Much confusion and controversy has resulted from this observation.

While some authors have attempted to explain the unbounded Sherwood and Nusselt numbers using models of uneven flow distributions in packed beds, it appears more likely that the effect is due to failure of most investigators to properly take into account axial dispersion in the analysis of their data. This effect is most pronounced at low Reynolds numbers in gas phase systems. Recently Wakao and Funazkri(34) corrected much of the previous mass transfer data for axial dispersion and found that the corrected results were well described by the equation:

$$N_{Sh_p} = 2 + 1.1 \, N_{Sc_f}^{1/3} N_{Re_p}^{0.6} \qquad (34)$$

thus confirming the concept of a limiting Sherwood number.

For heat transfer calculations it is recommended that Equation 34 be used with N_{Nu_p} and N_{Pr_f}, replacing N_{Sh_p} and N_{Sc_f} respectively. The resulting value of h_c would be a true convective heat transfer coefficient. Additional heat transfer due to radiation and conduction may have to be considered separately.

NOMENCLATURE

C	=	Concentration, gmol/cc.
C_p	=	Heat capacity, cal/g K.
d_p	=	Particle diameter, cm.
d_t	=	Bed diameter, cm.
D	=	Mass dispersion coefficient, cm²/s.
D_m	=	Molecular diffusion coefficient, cm²/s.
e	=	Emissivity
h_c	=	Convective heat transfer coefficient, cal/cm²·s K.
h_{rs}	=	Heat transfer coefficient due to solid-solid radiation, Equation 19, cal/cm²·s K.
h_{rv}	=	Heat transfer coefficient due to void-void radiation, Equation 20, cal/cm²·s K.
h_w	=	Wall heat transfer coefficient, cal/cm²·s K.
k_c	=	Convective mass transfer coefficient, cm/s.
N	=	Molar flux, gmol/cm²·s.
N_{Nu_p}	=	$h_c d_p/\lambda_f$ = Particle Nusselt number.
N_{Nu_w}	=	$h_w d_p/\lambda_f$ = Nusselt number for wall heat transfer.
P_b	=	"Break-away" pressure, Equation 24, atm.
N_{Pe_c}	=	A convective Peclet number, Table 2.
$N_{Pe_{h,r,p}}$	=	$d_p u \rho C_p/\lambda_r$ = Particle Peclet number for heat transfer in radial direction.
$N_{Pe_{h,z,p}}$	=	$d_p u \rho C_p/\lambda_z$ = Particle Peclet number for heat transfer in axial direction.
$N_{Pe_{m,r,p}}$	=	$u d_p/D_r$ = Particle Peclet number for mass transfer in radial direction.
$N_{Pe_{m,z,p}}$	=	$u d_p/D_z$ = Particle Peclet number for mass transfer in axial direction.
N_{Pr_f}	=	$C_p \mu/\lambda_f$ = Fluid Prandtl number.
N_{Pr_r}	=	$C_p \mu/\lambda_r$ = Prandtl number for radial thermal conduction.
p	=	Probability, Table 1.
q	=	Heat flux, cal/cm²·s.
N_{Re_p}	=	$d_p u \rho/\mu$ = Particle Reynolds number.
r	=	Radial coordinate, cm.
N_{Sc_f}	=	$\mu/\rho D_m$ = Molecular Schmidt number.
N_{Sc_r}	=	$\mu/\rho D_r$ = Schmidt number for radial mass dispersion.
N_{Sh_p}	=	$k_c d_p/D_m$ = Particle Sherwood number.
T	=	Absolute temperature, K.
u	=	Superficial velocity, cm/s.
x	=	Function defined by Equation 9.
z	=	Length coordinate, cm.

Greek Letters:

α	=	$1/N_{Pe_{m,r,p}}$ = Ranz's lateral displacement factor.
β	=	Empirical parameter, Equation 7.
ε	=	Bed porosity.
λ	=	Thermal conductivity, cal/cm·s K.
λ^f	=	Flow contribution to bed thermal conductivity, Equation 17, cal/cm·s K.
λ^o	=	Bed thermal conductivity in motionless fluid, Equation 18, cal/cm·s K.
μ	=	Viscosity, Poise.
ρ	=	Fluid density.
σ	=	Stefan-Boltzmann constant.
	=	Molecular diameter (Equation 24), cm.
τ	=	Tortuosity.
ψ	=	Film thickness @ point contacts/particle diameter.

Subscripts:

A	=	Component A.
B	=	Bulk fluid quantity.
f	=	Fluid quantity.
S	=	Surface quantity.
s	=	Solid quantity.
w	=	Wall quantity.

LITERATURE CITED

1. Schwartz, C. E. and J. M. Smith, *Ind. Eng. Chem.* 45, 1209 (1953).
2. Lerou, J. J. and G. F. Froment, *Chem. Eng. Sci.* 32, 853 (1977).
3. Schlünder, E. U., *ACS Symp. Ser.* 72, 110 (1978).
4. Levenspiel, O. and W. K. Smith, *Chem. Eng. Sci.* 6, 227 (1957).
5. Haynes, H. W., Jr., *Chem. Eng. Sci.* 32, 678 (1977).
6. Levenspiel, O., "Chemical Reaction Engineering," 2nd ed., John Wiley & Sons, Inc., New York, 1972.
7. Hays, J. R., W. C. Clements, Jr., and T. R. Harris, *AIChE J.* 13, 374 (1967).
8. Van der Laan, E. T., *Chem. Eng. Sci.,* 7, 187 (1958).
9. Gunn, D. J., *The Chem. Engr.* CE153 (1968).
10. Wen, C. Y. and L. T. Fan, "Models for Flow Systems and Chemical Reactors," Marcel Dekker, Inc., New York (1975).
11. Edwards, M. F. and J. F. Richardson, *Chem. Eng. Sci.* 23, 109 (1968).
12. Gunn, D. J., *Trans. Instn. Chem. Engrs.* 47, T351 (1969).
13. Miyauchi, T. and T. Kikuchi, *Chem. Eng. Sci.* 30, 343 (1975).
14. Bischoff, K. B. and O. Levenspiel, *Chem. Eng. Sci.* 17, 245 (1962).
15. Roemer, G., J. S. Dranoff and J. M. Smith, *Ind. Eng. Chem., Funds.* 1, 284 (1962).
16. Ranz, W. E., *Chem. Eng. Prog.* 48(5), 247 (1952).
17. Leva, M. and M. Grummer, *Ind. Eng. Chem.* 40, 415 (1948).
18. Gunn, D. J. and M. Khalid, *Chem. Eng. Sci.* 30, 261 (1975).
19. Gros, J. B. and R. Bugarel, *Int. Cong. Ch. Engr., Ch. Equip. Des. Auto., 5th*, paper K2.3, Prague, 1975.
20. Argo, W. B. and J. M. Smith, *Chem. Eng. Prog.* 49(8), 443 (1953).
21. Yagi, S. and D. Kunii, *AIChE J.* 3, 373 (1957).
22. Bauer, R. and E. U. Schlünder, *Int. Chem. Engr.* 18, 181 (1978); ibid 18, 189 (1978).
23. Smith, J. M., "Chemical Engineering Kinetics," 2nd ed., McGraw-Hill, New York (1970).
24. Bhattacharyya, D. and D. C. T. Pei, *Chem. Eng. Sci.* 30, 293 (1975).
25. Beek, J., *Adv. Chem. Engr.* 3, 203 (1962).
26. Schotte, W., *AIChE J.* 6, 63 (1960).
27. Gunn, D. J. and J. F. C. de Souza, *Chem. Eng. Sci.* 29, 1363 (1974).
28. Yagi, S. and N. Wakao, *AIChE J.* 5, 79 (1959).
29. Valstar, J. M., J. D. Bik and P. J. Van den Berg, *The Chem. Engr.* CE137 (1969).
30. Yagi, S. and D. Junii, *AIChE J.* 6, 97 (1960).
31. Hsiung, T. H. and G. Thodos, *Int. J. Heat Mass Trans.* 20, 331 (1977).
32. Sen Gupta, A. and G. Thodos, *AIChE J.* 8, 608 (1962).
33. Kunii, D. and M. Suzuki, *Int. J. Heat Mass Trans.* 10, 845 (1967).
34. Wakao, N. and T. Funazkri, *Chem. Eng. Sci.* 33, 1375 (1978).
35. Kwong, S. S. and J. M. Smith, *Ind. Eng. Chem.* 49, 894 (1957).

STUDY PROBLEMS

1. Under what circumstances would you expect that the correlations presented for the bed transport parameters might not be applicable?

2. Why are the bed transport parameters generally directionally dependent? Are there circumstances in which it might be reasonable to assume that they are independent of direction?

3. Plots of the mass transfer Peclet numbers versus Reynolds number are different for gases and liquids. Explain.

4. The well-known analogies between mass and heat transfer may not be applicable to packed beds. Why?

5. List the heat transfer mechanisms that might contribute to the effective thermal conductivity in packed beds.

6. Suggest a reason or reasons why there is so much uncertainty in correlations for the wall heat transfer coefficient.

7. What question is now being debated in the literature with regard to correlations for the external particle transport coefficients? Suggest a possible resolution to this question.

HOMEWORK PROBLEMS

1. At high velocities (i.e. for small deviations from plug flow) a packed bed reactor behaves very much like a series of stirred tanks. In this limit the residence time distributions for the axial dispersion model and the n-tanks-in-series model are identical and Gaussian. It may be considered that each void space represents a perfectly mixed cell. The mean residence time in a cell is $\bar{t}_i = l\epsilon/u$ where l is the length of a mixing cell. As an approximation:

$$l \cong \frac{L}{n} \cong d_p$$

Obtain a numerical estimate of the Peclet number, $N_{Pe_{m,z,p}}$, under these circumstances by equating variances for the two models.

2. It has been stated(35) that "the heat transfer characteristics of a packed bed cannot be greatly improved by changing the packing material." Let's investigate the sensitivity of the radial thermal conductivity to values of λ_s by calculations based on the Yagi and Kunii model. Calculate the ratio $(\lambda_r)_{\text{alumina}}/(\lambda_r)_{\text{steel}}$ as a function of $0 \leq N_{Re_p} \leq 1000$ for air flowing through a packed bed at an average temperature of 150 °C and one atmosphere pressure. The bed porosity may be taken as $\epsilon = 0.45$.

3. Calculate the ratio $(\lambda_r)_{NH_3}/(\lambda_r)_{\text{air}}$ as a function of $0 \leq N_{Re_p} \leq 1000$ for a bed of alumina particles at 150 °C and one atmosphere. The bed porosity is $\epsilon = 0.45$. Comment on the effect of fluid properties on the bed thermal conductivity.

4. Calculate the radial effective thermal conductivity for air flowing over a bed of half inch diameter alumina particles at 425 °C and one atmosphere pressure for $0 \leq N_{Re_p} \leq 1000$. The bed porosity is 0.45 and the emissivity, $e = 0.5$. Recompute, neglecting the radiation terms and compare.

5. Consider mass transfer from a single spherical particle immersed in a motionless fluid. Calculate the Sherwood number.

Module E3.6

Heat and Mass Transfer in Packed Beds-II

H. W. Haynes, Jr.

Department of Chemical Engineering
University of Wyoming
Laramie, WY 82071

OBJECTIVES
Upon completion of this module, the student should be able to:
1. Select an appropriate simplified reactor model for a particular application by applying various diagnostic tests for axial dispersion and nonisothermal behavior.
2. Calculate the conversion and temperature profiles from packed bed reactor models of varying complexity.

PREREQUISITE MATHEMATICAL SKILLS
1. Elementary calculus through differential equations.
2. Numerical analysis-solution to ODE by Runge-Kutta algorithm, solution to parabolic PDE by Crank-Nicolson algorithm and inversion of tridiagonal matrix by method of Thomas.

PREREQUISITE ENGINEERING AND SCIENCE SKILLS
1. Transport phenomena—mass and heat transfer in packed beds (Module E3.5).
2. Diffusion and reaction in porous media (Modules E3.1–E3.4).

This module will be concerned about developing differential energy and mass balance equations which describe chemical reactions in a packed bed reactor. Utilizing a reactor model that possesses a high degree of generality, this module will show how simplifications can be effected in order to obtain equations which are more amenable to solution. The advantages of this approach are two-fold. First, it allows the identification of many parameters which, depending upon the conditions of operation, may enter into the problem. Secondly, it forces one to recognize the approximations contained in the final model.

QUASI-CONTINUUM MODEL—GENERAL FORMULATION

In a large packed bed reactor, one can, to a good approximation, consider the concentration and temperature profiles to be continuous functions of the length coordinates. The mixing of fluid elements that occurs on a scale of the order of the catalyst particle size can be accounted for by a diffusive or dispersive type of mechanism. Since the bulk fluid flows in the axial direction, the dispersion of mass and energy is directionally dependent, i.e. the bed is anisotropic. The "general formulation" presented here is not truly general since the restrictive assumptions listed in Table 1 are incorporated into the model.

Consider the volume element identified in Figure 1. When one carries out a steady-state component A (reactant) mass balance, and then considers the limits as Δz and Δr approach zero, the following is obtained:

$$D_z \frac{\partial^2 C_A}{\partial z^2} - u \frac{\partial C_A}{\partial z} + \frac{D_r}{r} \frac{\partial}{\partial r}\left(r \frac{\partial C_A}{\partial r}\right)$$
$$+ \eta' \rho_p R_{AW} = 0 \qquad (1)$$

Where D_z and D_r are the Fick's law dispersion coefficients in the axial and radial directions, respectively, and η' is the effectiveness factor relative to bulk fluid properties (See E3.4). Other quantities are defined in the Nomenclature. The energy balance on the same volume element is:

$$\lambda_z \frac{\partial^2 T}{\partial z^2} - u\rho C_P \frac{\partial T}{\partial z} + \frac{\lambda_r}{r} \frac{\partial}{\partial r}\left(r \frac{\partial T}{\partial r}\right)$$
$$+ \eta' \rho_b R_{AW} \Delta H_r = 0 \qquad (2)$$

In this equation, λ_z and λ_r are the effective bed thermal conductivities in the axial and radial directions; u is the superficial velocity. Note that η' and R_{AW} are functions of the bulk fluid temperature and concentration.

It is instructive to make Equations 1 and 2 dimensionless by introducing the variables:

$$X = (C_{AO} - C_A)/C_{AO} \qquad (3)$$

ISSN 0270-7659/81/0516-0040/$04.30/0 © 1982, American Institute of Chemical Engineers.

Table 1. Assumptions inherent in "General Formulation" of the quasi-continuum model of a packed bed reactor.

Assumption	Comments
Anisotropic Continuum	Valid for $d_t/d_p > 10$ and $L/d_p > 6(1)$.
Uniform Radial Velocity Profile	Valid for $d_t/d_p > 30$. Enhanced velocity at the wall must be considered for highly exothermic reactions in beds characterized by small tube/particle diameter ratios(2).
Constant Physical Properties	Some variation in radial heat and mass transfer Peclet numbers can be expected for low d_t/d_p ratios(3). Temperature dependence of quantities such as ΔH_r, C_p, D_A^e, etc., could be included in the model with little increase in complexity, but these effects are usually of secondary importance—highly exothermic reactions excepted.
Constant Density	Assumed for convenience in presentation. Variable density problems can be treated with little increased complexity.
Single Reaction	Assumed for convenience in presentation.
Power Law Kinetics	Assumed for illustrative purposes. Other rate expressions can be readily incorporated into the model.
Constant Wall Temperature	Practical when cooling medium is constant boiling bath. Can be removed with some increase in complexity.

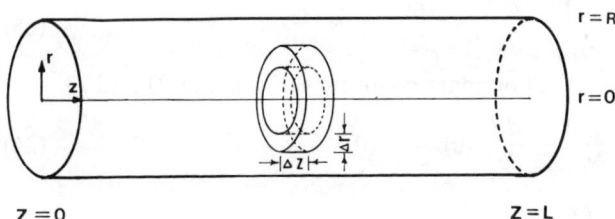

Figure 1. Differential volume element for steady state mass balance.

$$T^* = T/T_o \quad (4)$$

$$z^* = z/L \quad (5)$$

$$r^* = r/R \quad (6)$$

Then,
$$\frac{1}{N_{Pe_{m,z,L}}} \frac{\partial^2 X}{\partial z^{*2}} - \frac{\partial X}{\partial z^*} + \frac{L/R}{N_{Pe_{m,r,R}}} \frac{1}{r^*} \frac{\partial}{\partial r^*}\left(r^* \frac{\partial X}{\partial r^*}\right)$$
$$- \eta' R^* = 0 \quad (7)$$

and
$$\frac{1}{N_{Pe_{h,z,L}}} \frac{\partial^2 T^*}{\partial z^{*2}} - \frac{\partial T^*}{\partial z^*} + \frac{L/R}{N_{Pe_{h,r,R}}} \frac{1}{r^*} \frac{\partial}{\partial r^*}\left(r^* \frac{\partial T^*}{\partial r^*}\right)$$
$$+ \Delta H^* \eta' R^* = 0 \quad (8)$$

The dimensionless parameters will be summarized later. The dimensionless reaction rate, R^*, is given by:

$$R^* = \frac{L\rho_b R_{AW}}{uC_{AO}} = R^*(X,T^*) \quad (9)$$

For power law kinetics, $-R_{AW} = kC_A^n$, and

$$-R^* = N_{Da} \exp\left[-\gamma_o\left(\frac{1}{T^*} - 1\right)\right](1 - X)^n \quad (10)$$

Here, the Arrhenius equation is used to relate the rate constant, k, to the inlet value, k_o, i.e.

$$\frac{k}{k_o} = \exp\left[-\gamma_o\left(\frac{1}{T^*} - 1\right)\right] \quad (11)$$

The effectiveness factor was considered in previous modules. For power law kinetics:

$$\eta' = \eta'(X,T^*,n,h',\gamma',\beta',N_{Bi_m}, N_{Bi_h}) \quad (12)$$

The primed quantities, it is recalled, are based upon local bulk fluid conditions. For the present application it is more convenient to consider parameters calculated from inlet fluid properties, i.e.,

$$\eta' = \eta'(X,T^*,n,h_o,\gamma_o,\beta_o,N_{Bi_m}, N_{Bi_h}) \quad (13)$$

It follows from the definitions of the various parameters that:

$$h' = h_o \exp\left[-\frac{1}{2}\gamma_o\left(\frac{1}{T^*} - 1\right)\right](1 - X)^{\frac{n-1}{2}} \quad (14)$$

$$\gamma' = \gamma_o/T^* \quad (15)$$

$$\beta' = \beta_o(1 - X)/T^* \quad (16)$$

Attention can now be paid to the boundary conditions for use with Equations 7 and 8. Since no net flux of mass or energy is present at the reactor centerline,

$$\frac{\partial X}{\partial r^*}(z^*,0) = 0 \quad (17)$$

$$\frac{\partial T^*}{\partial r^*}(z^*,0) = 0 \quad (18)$$

A similar situation exists at the wall regarding mass transfer, but provision must be made for convective wall heat transfer if the reactor operates nonadiabatically. Thus:

$$\frac{\partial X}{\partial r^*}(z^*,1) = 0 \quad (19)$$

$$\frac{\partial T^*}{\partial r^*}(z^*,1) = -N_{Bi_w}[T^*(z^*,1) - T_W^*] \quad (20)$$

where T_W^* is the dimensionless wall temperature (assumed constant). Not so straight forward, are the boundary conditions at the reactor inlet. The rigorous boundary conditions were derived by Young and

Finlayson, but they are very complex(4). For applications they recommend the approximate boundary conditions obtained by the orthogonal collocation method:

$$\frac{1}{N_{Pe_{m,z,L}}}\frac{\partial X}{\partial z^*}(0,r^*) = X(0,r^*) \quad (21)$$

and

$$\frac{1}{N_{Pe_{h,z,L}}}\frac{\partial T^*}{\partial z^*}(0,r^*)$$
$$= \frac{1}{2}\left\{1 + \sqrt{1 + \frac{24(L/R)N_{Bi_W}}{(3 + N_{Bi_W})N_{Pe_{h,r,R}}N_{Pe_{h,z,L}}}}\right\}_A$$
$$\times [T^*(0,r^*) - 1] \quad (22)$$

The quantities in the brackets, $\{\ \}_A$, are evaluated in the section just upstream of the bed entrance. Equation 21 is the celebrated "Danckwerts boundary condition" at the inlet. To most, the forms of Equations 21 and 22 are not immediately obvious. Particularly upsetting is the fact that they imply discontinuities in concentration and temperature at the reactor inlet. Nevertheless, the explanation set forth by Wehner and Wilhelm for the isothermal reactor(5) should help clarify the situation. This problem is outlined in Homework Problem 1.

Young and Finlayson also derived approximate boundary conditions for the outlet:

$$\frac{\partial X}{\partial z^*}(1,r^*) = 0 \quad (23)$$

and

$$\frac{1}{N_{Pe_{h,z,L}}}\frac{\partial T^*}{\partial z^*}(1,r^*)$$
$$= \frac{1}{2}\left\{1 - \sqrt{1 + \frac{24(L/R)N_{Bi_W}}{(3 + Bi_W)N_{Pe_{h,r,R}}N_{Pe_{h,z,L}}}}\right\}_C$$
$$\times [T^*(1,r^*) - T_W^*] \quad (24)$$

The quantities in brackets, $\{\ \}_C$, are evaluated in the section just downstream of the bed exit. Equation 23 is the Danckwerts boundary condition at the bed outlet.

These equations, along the equations developed in Modules E3.2, E3.3 and E3.4, for calculating the effectiveness factor constitute a complete description of packed bed reactors when the assumptions in Table 1 are allowable. The dimensionless parameters which enter into the solution of this problem are summarized in Table 2. It is clear that many realistic combinations of parameters are possible, and thus a convenient method of solution is needed. However, the difficulty in obtaining a numerical solution to the general equations is quickly recognized when one recalls that a boundary value problem must be solved for every point in the reactor where a value of the effectiveness factor is required. While the numerical solution of the general equations is not beyond the capabilities of modern high speed computers, considerable savings in programming and computational efforts can be realized by making reasonable simplifications in the model prior to computation. The next section will examine a greatly simplified problem—the isothermal reactor. Subsequent sections will be concerned with reactors of increasing complexity.

ISOTHERMAL REACTOR

The isothermal packed bed reactor finds extensive use in the laboratory because of the ease with which isothermal kinetics can be interpreted. A large commercial packed bed reactor can be operated isothermally only when the heat of reaction is small or when a large heat transfer area is provided per unit bed volume. When neither of these options is feasible, one is forced to select some other reactor type, e.g. a fluidized bed reactor, to maintain isothermal conditions.

The equations for the isothermal reactor are relatively simple. The energy balance is eliminated, and no radial concentration gradients are present (when the velocity profile is flat). Equation 7 simplifies to:

$$\frac{1}{N_{Pem,z,L}}\frac{d^2X}{dz^{*2}} - \frac{dX}{dz^*} - \eta' R^* = 0 \quad (25)$$

with the boundary conditions, Equations 21 and 23:

$$\frac{1}{N_{Pem,z,L}}\frac{dX}{dz^*}(0) = X(0) \quad (26)$$

$$\frac{dX}{dz^*}(1) = 0 \quad (27)$$

Furthermore, assume that the catalyst particle temperature and concentrations are uniform at the bulk fluid values, i.e. that particle mass and heat transfer rates are rapid relative to the rate of reaction. Then η' is everywhere unity*. Upon substituting from Equation 10, for power law kinetics:

$$\frac{1}{N_{Pem,z,L}}\frac{d^2X}{dz^{*2}} - \frac{dX}{dz^*} + N_{Da}(1 - X)^n = 0 \quad (28)$$

For $n = 1$ the solution(5) is:

$$1 - X = \frac{4a \exp(N_{Pem,z,L}/2)}{(1 + a)^2 \exp(aN_{Pem,z,L}/2) - (1 - a)^2 \exp(-aN_{Pem,z,L}/2)} \quad (29)$$

where:

$$a = \sqrt{1 + 4N_{Da}/N_{Pem,z,L}} \quad (30)$$

Numerical approximations to Equation 25 are generally required when the rate expression is nonlinear.

At this point, one might naturally inquire about the importance of axial dispersion and how the solutions to Equations 26–28 compare with the plug flow model solutions for which:

$$-\frac{dX}{dz^*} + N_{Da}(1 - X)^n = 0 \quad (31)$$

$$X(0) = 0 \quad (32)$$

---

*Such reactor models are termed "homogeneous." In "heterogeneous" reactor models, the particle temperatures and/or concentrations will differ from the bulk fluid values as a consequence of finite intraparticle or external transport resistances.

Table 2. Parameters in general reactor design problem (Power Law Kinetics).

Parameter	Definition	
n	—	Reaction order
h_o	$l_o \sqrt{\dfrac{\rho_p k_o C_{AO}^{n-1}}{D_A^e}}$	Thiele modulus @ inlet
β_o	$\dfrac{(-\Delta H_r) D_A^e C_{AO}}{\lambda^e T_o}$	Particle adiabatic temperature rise @ inlet
γ_o	$\dfrac{E_a}{RT_o}$	Arrhenius number @ inlet
N_{Bi_m}	$\dfrac{l_o k_c}{D_A^e}$	Mass transfer particle Biot number
N_{Bi_h}	$\dfrac{l_o h_c}{\lambda^e}$	Heat transfer particle Biot number
L/R	—	Reactor aspect ratio
$N_{Pe_{m,z},L}$	$\dfrac{uL}{D_z}$	Axial Peclet number for mass transfer
$N_{Pe_{m,r},R}$	$\dfrac{uR}{D_r}$	Radial Peclet number for mass transfer
$N_{Pe_{h,z},L}$	$\dfrac{uL\rho C_p}{\lambda_z}$	Axial Peclet number for heat transfer
$N_{Pe_{h,r},R}$	$\dfrac{uR\rho C_p}{\lambda_r}$	Radial Peclet number for heat transfer
N_{Da}	$\dfrac{L\rho_b k_o C_{AO}^{n-1}}{u}$ $= \rho \tau_w k_o C_{AO}^{n-1}$	Damköhler number
ΔH^*	$\dfrac{C_{AO} -\Delta H_r}{\rho C_p T_o}$	Reactor adiabatic temperature rise
N_{Bi_W}	$\dfrac{h_w R}{\lambda_r}$	Wall Biot number

For positive reaction orders, the axial dispersion model always predicts decreased yields as compared with the plug flow model; or, viewed another way, more catalyst is required in an axially dispersed reactor to give a conversion equivalent to that in a plug flow reactor. But how significant is this correction when realistic values of the Peclet number are considered?

To aid in answering this question, make use of the criterion developed by Levenspiel and Bischoff(6) for equal conversions in plug flow and axially dispersed reactors ($n = 1$):

$$\frac{W}{W_{PF}} = 1 + N_{Da}/N_{Pe_{m,z},L} \quad (33)$$

As an example consider a packed bed reactor operating such that $N_{Re_p} > 10$. In this situation, as learned from the previous module, $N_{Pe_{m,z},p} = ud_p/D_z \cong 2$. Assuming one is dealing with a short laboratory reactor in which $L/d_p = 10$, then,

$$N_{Pe_{m,z},L} = \left(\frac{ud_p}{D_z}\right)\left(\frac{L}{d_p}\right) = 20$$

At the 95% conversion level, the following is obtained from Equations 31 and 32:

$$N_{Da} = -\ln(1 - X) = -\ln(1 - 0.95) = 2.99$$

Upon substituting into Equation 33, $W/W_{pf} = 1.15$. For this rather extreme example, the axially dispersed reactor requires a 15% increase in catalyst requirement over the plug flow reactor. For a more reasonable L/d_p ratio of say 100, the increased catalyst requirement due to axial dispersion is only 1.5% It can be concluded therefore, that *except for short laboratory reactors, the effects of axial dispersion in the isothermal packed bed reactor can be safely neglected.*

Mears(7) has developed a criterion for neglecting axial dispersion effects in packed bed reactors. For power law kinetics in an isothermal packed bed reactor, the criterion can be expressed as:

$$\frac{nN_{Da}}{N_{Pe_{m,z},L}} < 0.05 \quad (34)$$

This result (for $n = 1$) can be obtained from Equation 33, if one requires that the increased catalyst loading, due to axial dispersion, not exceed five percent. A useful test for isothermal operation was also developed by Mears(8). The bed can be assumed isothermal when the following inequality is satisfied:

$$\left| \frac{(1 + 0.4/N_{Bi_W})\gamma_O N_{Pe_{h,r,R}}\Delta H^* R^*}{(L/R)T_W^{*2}} \right| < 0.4 \quad (35)$$

where R^* is evaluated at the reactor depth of interest. For positive reaction orders, assuming isothermal behavior, the rate is greatest at the entrance to the bed.

ADIABATIC REACTOR

Very often when studying reactions with substantial heats of reaction, it is not possible to operate a packed bed reactor isothermally. That is especially true on the commercial scale, where the available heat transfer surface per unit bed volume may be quite small. When it is impractical to operate a laboratory reactor isothermally, it may be desirable to operate the reactor adiabatically. Adiabatic operation eliminates the need for dealing with radial variations in temperature and concentration, and thereby simplifies the data analysis greatly. Furthermore, the adiabatic laboratory or pilot plant reactor often simulates the commercial reactor more closely than an isothermal reactor.

For the adiabatic reactor Equations 7 and 8 reduce to:

$$\frac{1}{N_{Pe_{m,z,L}}} \frac{d^2 X}{dz^{*2}} - \frac{dX}{dz^*} - \eta' R^* = 0 \quad (36)$$

$$\frac{1}{N_{Pe_{h,z,L}}} \frac{d^2 T^*}{dz^{*2}} - \frac{dT^*}{dz^*} + \Delta H^* \eta' R^* = 0 \quad (37)$$

The boundary conditions for the mass balance are identical to the isothermal case, Equations 26 and 27. The boundary conditions for the energy balance are obtained from Equations 22 and 24 by setting $N_{Bi_W} = 0$:

$$\frac{1}{N_{Pe_{h,z,L}}} \frac{dT^*}{dz^*}(0) = T^*(0) - 1 \quad (38)$$

$$\frac{dT^*}{dz^*}(1) = 0 \quad (39)$$

By eliminating the product $\eta' R^*$ between Equations 36 and 37, and solving the resulting differential equation, a relation between X and T^* is obtained at the exit [Reference (9)]:

$$T^*(1) - 1 = -\Delta H^* X(1) \quad (40)$$

Furthermore, it can be shown that this linear relation between temperature and conversion is valid for any point with the reactor for equal mass and heat transfer Peclet numbers, $N_{Pe_{m,z,L}} = N_{Pe_{h,z,L}}$. In this event one of the differential equations, Equation 36 or 37, can be eliminated.

The maximum temperature difference across the reactor is obtained when $X(1) = 1$. Then Equation 40 becomes, after substituting the original variables,

$$\frac{T_{max} - T_O}{T_O} = -\Delta H^* \quad (41)$$

Thus $-\Delta H^*$ is the reactor adiabatic temperature rise. For endothermic reaction T_{max} must be replaced with T_{min}.

The problem is simplified greatly when it can be assumed that $\eta' = 1$. It is still not possible, however, to obtain an analytical solution due principally to the nonlinear temperature dependence of the rate constant(s) contained in R^*. Fortunately, the homogeneous problem can be handled by a number of numerical techniques, and a particularly convenient method of solution is outlined in Reference (9).

Comparisons of axial dispersion model calculations with the plug flow model have indicated that the axial dispersion contribution is small for most reactions of industrial importance(10). Mears(11) has extended his criterion for neglecting axial dispersion to nonisothermal reactors:

$$\left| \frac{nN_{Da}}{N_{Pe_{m,z,L}}} - \frac{\gamma_O(-\Delta H^*)N_{Da}}{T^* T_W^* N_{Pe_{h,z,L}}} \right| < 0.05 \quad (42)$$

where T^* is a value inside the bed and can be calculated using the plug flow model. For adiabatic reactors $T_W^* = T^*$. While it is often reasonable to neglect axial dispersion in the adiabatic reactor, it is clear from the heat transfer term in Equation 42 that axial dispersion becomes significant for systems characterized by a high adiabatic temperature rise and strong axial heat conduction. In fact, axial dispersion can lead to multiple steady states in such systems(12,13).

NONADIABATIC-NONISOTHERMAL REACTOR

When heat effects are very large, as with many oxidation reactions for example, it may not be possible to operate a packed bed reactor either isothermally or adiabatically. The adiabatic temperature rise may be so large as to exceed the materials of construction limitations on the reactor, the catalyst may be damaged, or undesirable side reactions may become a problem. Attempts to cool the reactor may only be partially successful due to the finite thermal conductivity of the bed and the heat transfer resistance at the wall. Such reactions are usually carried out in small diameter tubular heat exchangers as a means of maximizing the ratio of heat transfer area to bed volume. Radial variations in temperature and concentration must be recognized in these systems, and all the terms in Equations 7 and 8 must be kept in order to provide a complete description of the reactor. However approximations are useful for describing many features of the NANIR and in some cases an approximate design is all that is warranted by uncertainties in the design parameter.

One-Dimensional Model:

In formulating the one-dimensional model of the NANIR, the complexities arising from radial temperature and concentration gradients are avoided by lumping all resistance to heat transfer at the wall. Furthermore, it is common practice to omit the axial dispersion terms. The justification for this is open to some criticism and will be discussed later. With these rather stringent assumptions, the mass and energy balances are:

$$-\frac{dX}{dz^*} - R^* = 0 \qquad (43)$$

and

$$-\frac{dT^*}{dz^*} + \Delta H^* R^* - \frac{(L/R)N_{\overline{Bi}_w}}{N_{Pe_{h,r,R}}}(T^* - T_w^*) = 0 \qquad (44)$$

Here, it has also been assumed that the reactor is homogeneous, i.e. $\eta' = 1$. The quantity $N_{\overline{Bi}_w}$ in Equation 44 is a wall Biot number based on the lumped wall heat transfer coefficient, $\overline{h}_w$. The lumped heat transfer coefficient is a function of the true wall heat transfer coefficient, h_w, and the effective bed thermal conductivity, λ_r. Either of the expressions:

$$\frac{1}{\overline{h}_w} = \frac{1}{h_w} + \frac{R}{4\lambda_r}$$

or

$$\frac{1}{\overline{h}_w} = \frac{1}{h_w} + \frac{R}{3\lambda_r}$$

are commonly used to express this relationship (e.g. *4*, *14*). In terms of dimensionless quantities, the relationship is:

$$\frac{1}{N_{\overline{Bi}_w}} = \frac{1}{N_{Bi_w}} + \frac{1}{4} \qquad (45)$$

or

$$\frac{1}{N_{\overline{Bi}_w}} = \frac{1}{N_{Bi_w}} + \frac{1}{3} \qquad (46)$$

Equations 43 and 44 with the initial conditions, $X(0) = 0$ and $T^*(0) = 1$, are readily solved by the Runge-Kutta Technique.

Two-Dimensional Model:

By its very nature, the one-dimensional model cannot provide detailed information about the temperature and conversion profiles within the NANIR. The two-dimensional model takes into account radial variations and thus it is a much more realistic model of the reactor. Again, one neglects axial dispersion of heat and mass and writes for the homogeneous case:

$$-\frac{\partial X}{\partial z^*} + \frac{L/R}{N_{Pe_{m,r,R}}} \frac{1}{r^*}\left(r^* \frac{\partial X}{\partial r^*}\right) - R^* = 0 \qquad (47)$$

and

$$-\frac{\partial T^*}{\partial z^*} + \frac{L/R}{N_{Pe_{h,r,R}}} \frac{1}{r^*}\left(r^* \frac{\partial T^*}{\partial r^*}\right) + \Delta H^* R^* = 0 \qquad (48)$$

subject to the boundary conditions, Equations 17–20 and the initial conditions $X(0) = 0$, $T^*(0) = 1$. These equations constitute a set of nonlinear partial differential equations of the parabolic type. The most widely employed method of solution appears to be any of several variations of the Crank-Nicolson scheme de-

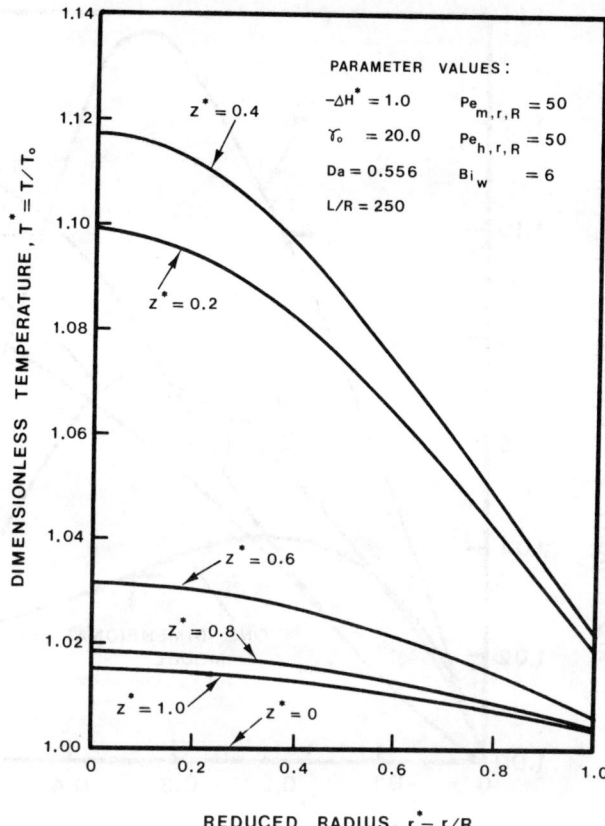

Figure 2. Radial temperature profiles, two-dimensional plug flow model, first-order reaction ($T_W = T_O$).

pending upon the manner in which the nonlinear rate term is handled(*15*). A computer program based upon this approach is available.*

The results from a two-dimensional model calculation are illustrated in Figures 2 and 3. One-dimensional model results are also plotted in Figure 3 for comparison purposes. For the two-dimensional model, the average temperature is calculated from:

$$T^*_{avg} = 2 \int_0^1 T^* r^* dr^* \qquad (49)$$

These results are in agreement with Froment's observation that "except for mild conditions," the one dimensional model may "fail to predict the mean temperatures and that the predicted values are always low for exothermic reactions"(*14*). It is clear from the large radial variations in temperature, Figure 1, that the small increase in computation time for the two-dimensional model relative to that of the one-dimensional model is justified.

Importance of Axial Dispersion:

The two-dimensional model discussed in the previous section has found wide use in simulating nonadiabatic nonisothermal packed bed reactors. Where comparisons

---
*Program is called REDS2, designed for use on a DEC System 10. The language used is Normal FORTRAN. For a copy of the program, write Educational Services Dept., AIChE, 345 E. 47th St., NY, NY 10017. Specify REDS2 (Module E3.6). Price of the program is $1.00.

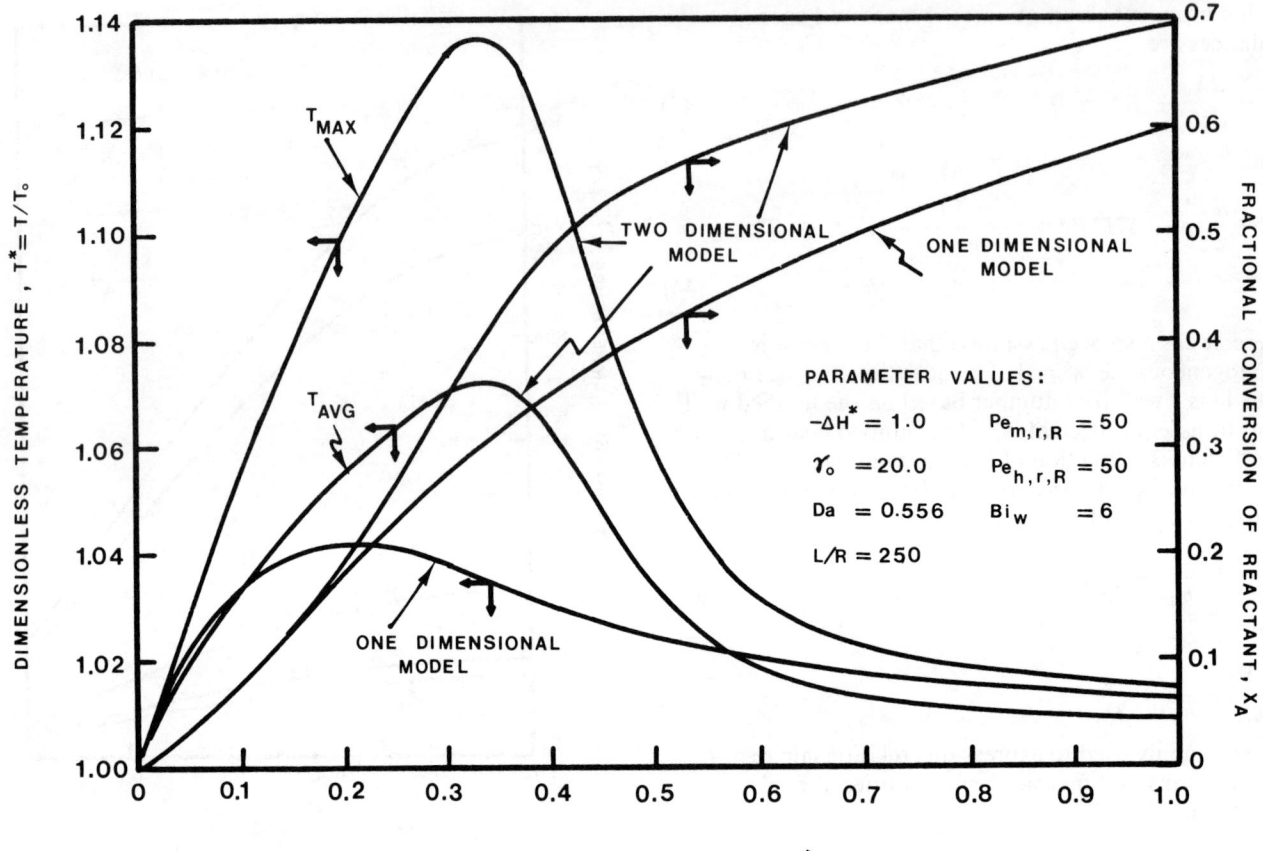

Figure 3. Axial temperature and conversion profiles, first-order reaction ($T_W = T_O$).

of the calculations with experimental temperature profiles have been undertaken, the deviations are within a range which can be explained by uncertainties in the parameter values(16). Such observations would hardly seem to warrant further improvements in the model in view of the computational complexities which result.

However, in recent years the orthogonal collocation method has been applied with remarkable success to problems in chemical reactor design(17). Young and Finlayson used orthogonal collocation to obtain solutions to the general homogeneous model, Equations 7 and 8 for $\eta' = 1$(4). So it no longer seems *necessary* to drop the axial dispersion terms in order to avoid computational difficulties.

Young and Finlayson made some interesting points regarding axial dispersion effects in the NANIR. Whereas axial dispersion is seldom of importance in isothermal and adiabatic reactors it does not follow that the axial dispersion terms can be neglected in the NANIR design. If the reactor is long enough the conversion in isothermal and adiabatic reactors will reach an ultimate predictable value irrespective of whether the axial dispersion terms are retained. In the NANIR, on the other hand, cooling in the vicinity of the inlet can quench the reaction so that the ultimate conversion level is never attained at any reactor length. If the reactor is operating in a region of parametric sensitivity then a few degrees variation in inlet temperature can have drastic effects on performance as is

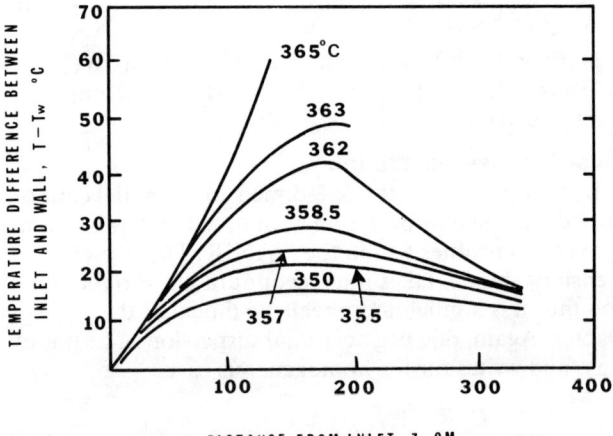

Figure 4. Temperature profiles for various inlet temperatures. A one-dimensional model of o-xylene oxidation reaction(14).

evident from Figure 4. Under such circumstances axial dispersion should be considered in the reactor design.

Young and Finlayson reinvestigated the sulfur dioxide oxidation reactor design example in the text by J. M. Smith(2). In the example the inlet temperature was measured for the case of cooling with no reaction and found to vary radially. The radial variation of inlet temperatures is not consistent with the two-dimensional initial value problem for which $T^*(0) = 1$, and provides strong evidence for a significant contribution due to axial dispersion. Radial variations of inlet temperatures are consistent with the boundary condition given by Equation 22. The question arises as to what initial condition to use when solving the two dimensional model equations, Equations 47 and 48, when the experimental inlet temperature profile is available. Interestingly (and fortunately, from the standpoint of *a priori* design) numerical comparisons with the general model solutions indicated that the flat profile, $T^*(0) = 1$, should be used in preference to the experimental profile.

HETEROGENEOUS MODELS

Reference has already been made to the vast computational effort to be undertaken, should it be found necessary to solve the boundary value problems associated with individual catalyst particles at every grid point within a two-dimensional reactor. In fact, there do not appear to be any examples in the literature where such an approach has been taken for nonlinear reactions in nonisothermal particles. Throw in the possibility that external transport resistance might be significant and the problem borders upon a state of being unmanageable. Clearly a careful ordering of priorities regarding the significant transport effects associated with individual catalyst particles will pay substantial dividends.

In Module E3.4, diagnostic criteria were presented and used to evaluate the relative significance of the various transport resistances associated with a single catalyst particle (See also Homework Problem 5 of Module E3.4). For isothermal reactions, it was shown that intraparticle mass transfer resistances are more likely to be significant than are external mass transfer resistances. For moderately exothermic reactions ($\gamma\beta/n \cong 1$) the order of decreasing significance of the transport resistances is: *External heat transfer > intraparticle mass transfer $\cong$ intraparticle heat transfer > external mass transfer*, and for strongly exothermic reactions ($\gamma\beta/n > 1$) the order is: *external heat transfer > intraparticle heat transfer > intraparticle mass transfer > external mass transfer*. The criteria provide useful internal tests for evaluating significant transport resistances in heterogeneous model computations.

As this discussion indicates, it can often be assumed, and with good justification, that the pellet is isothermal. The temperature may, however, be different from the bulk fluid temperature. For a first-order isothermal reaction, an analytical expression for the effectiveness factor was obtained. For arbitrary kinetics a good approximation to the effectiveness factor can usually be obtained using the Generalized Thiele modulus (See Module E3.2). It is important that the pellet material balance equations, or approximations to these equations, be analytically solvable. Otherwise the effectiveness factors must be obtained by cumbersome interpolations from numerical data or by solving the intrapellet boundary value problems as they are encountered. Iterative computations become necessary when external transport resistances are significant (See Module E3.4).

In a recent examination of the isothermal pellet assumption for the naphthalene oxidation reaction it was determined that the assumption was valid for small pellets (≈ 0.15 cm diameter). However, for large particles (≈ 0.5 cm diameter) with large effective diffusivities the isothermal pellet assumption was found to be in error(*18*). Approximate expressions are available for the effectiveness factor in nonisothermal particles (See Module E3.4).

COMMENTS ON REACTOR STABILITY

Reactor stability means different things to different authors. To some, an unstable reactor is one which operates in a region of "parametric sensitivity," where a small change in a design parameter or a process variable can have drastic effects on the operating state of the reactor. To others an unstable reactor is one which operates in a region where multiple steady states are possible. In either case reactor runaway is possible with the introduction of a disturbance into the system. Parametric sensitivity is probably of more concern from the standpoint of safety because one usually finds that a region of multiplicity is preceded by a region of parametric sensitivity.

An example of parametric sensitivity in the NANIR is provided in Figure 4. These results were computed by Froment for the gas phase air oxidation of o-xylene to phthalic anhydride using the one-dimensional homogeneous reactor model(*14*). The sensitivity of this system to small variations in inlet temperature is vividly demonstrated. Attempts to increase conversion by increasing the inlet temperature could result in disastrous consequences. Results such as this are quite sobering when one recognizes the large amount of uncertainty in values of the design parameters. Computations are particularly sensitive to the radial heat transport parameters(*14,19*). Diagnostic tests are available for defining regions of parametric sensitivity (e.g. *20, 21*), but simulations using the one-dimensional, or preferably the two-dimensional model, are more revealing. Parametric sensitivity regions associated with individual catalyst particles must also be considered(*22*).

Steady-state multiplicities are predicted by the axial dispersion model, and indeed multiple steady states have been observed experimentally in adiabatic and nonadiabatic, nonisothermal reactors(*12,13,23*). Diagnostic criteria are available for predicting the region of multiple steady states, (e.g. *24, 25*) or alternatively the solutions can be mapped(*26*). In early studies it was concluded that multiplicities in adiabatic reactors were limited to very short beds, but more recent work which takes into account known differences in heat and mass transfer Peclet numbers has revealed a much expanded region of multiple steady states(*9*). Multiple steady states in nonisothermal reactors can arise from heat and mass transfer resistances associated with individual catalyst particles. Thus a heterogeneous plug flow model of the adiabatic reactor will, for appropriate parameter values, predict multiple steady states. In one experimental study of the adiabatic packed bed reactor, it was concluded that axial heat and mass dispersion along with interparticle and intraparticle effects were required to predict the extinction point, i.e. the point of return to the low temperature steady state(*13*). The homogeneous models predicted the ignition point quite accurately.

NOMENCLATURE

a	=	Parameter defined by Equation 30.
N_{Bi}	=	Biot number, Table 2.
C_A	=	Concentration, gmol/cc.
C_p	=	Heat capacity at constant pressure, cal/gm·K.
d_p	=	Particle diameter, cm.
d_t	=	Bed diameter, cm.
D	=	Mass dispersion coefficient, cm^2/s.
D_A^e	=	Effective diffusivity, cm^2/s.
h	=	Thiele modulus, Table 2.
h_W	=	Wall heat transfer coefficient.
k	=	Rate constant, dimensions vary.
L	=	Bed length, cm.
l_O	=	Particle length parameter, cm.
n	=	Reaction order, power law kinetics.
N_{Da}	=	Damköhler number, Table 2.
N_{Pe}	=	Peclet number, Table 2.
R	=	Bed radius, cm.
R^*	=	Dimensionless reaction rate, Equation 9.
R_{AW}	=	Molar rate of formation of component A, gmol/gm·s.
r	=	Radial coordinate, cm.
r^*	=	Dimensionless radial coordinate, Equation 6.
T	=	Absolute temperature, K.
T^*	=	Dimensionless temperature, Equation 4.
u	=	Superficial velocity, cm/s.
X	=	Fractional conversion, Equation 3.
z	=	Length coordinate, cm.
z^*	=	Dimensionless length coordinate, Equation 5.

Greek Letters:

β	=	Particle adiabatic temperature Rise, Table 2.
γ	=	Arrhenius number, Table 2.
$-\Delta H^*$	=	Reactor adiabatic temperature rise, Table 2.
ΔH_r	=	Heat of reaction, cal/gmol.
η'	=	Effectiveness factor based on bulk fluid properties.
λ	=	Bed thermal conductivity, cal/cm·s·K.
λ^e	=	Particle effective thermal conductivity, cal/cm·s·K.
ρ	=	Fluid density, gm/cc.
ρ_b	=	Catalyst bed density, gm/cc.
τ_W	=	Space time, gm/(gm/hr).

Subscripts:

h	=	heat transfer quantity.
m	=	mass transfer quantity.
o	=	inlet value.
r	=	radial direction.
z	=	axial direction.

LITERATURE CITED

1. Hlavacek, V., *Ind. Eng. Chem.* 62, 8 (1970).
2. Smith, J. M., "Chemical Engineering Kinetics," 2nd ed., McGraw-Hill (1970).
3. Olbrich, W. E. and O. E. Potter, *Chem. Eng. Sci.* 27, 1723 (1972).
4. Young, L. C. and B. A. Finlayson, *Ind. Eng. Chem., Fund.* 12, 412 (1973).
5. Wehner, J. F. and R. H. Wilhelm, *Chem. Eng. Sci.* 6, 89 (1956).
6. Levenspiel, O. and K. B. Bischoff, *Adv. Chem. Eng.* 4, 95 (1963).
7. Mears, D. E., *Chem. Eng. Sci.* 26, 1361 (1971).
8. Mears, D. E., *J. Catal.* 20, 127 (1971); *Ind. Eng. Chem., Proc. Des. Dev.* 10, 541 (1971).
9. Hlavacek, V. and J. Votruba, "Steady-State Operation of Fixed-Bed Reactors and Monolithic Structures," in "Chemical Reactor Theory: A Review," Lapidus, L. and N. R. Amundson, Eds., Prentice-Hall, Englewood Cliffs, New Jersey (1977).
10. Carberry, J. J. and M. M. Wendel, *AIChE J.* 9, 129 (1963).
11. Mears, D. E., *Ind. Eng. Chem., Fund.* 15, 20 (1976).
12. Wicke, E. and G. Padberg, *Chem. Eng. Sci.* 22, 1035 (1967).
13. Hlavacek, V. and J. Votruba, *Adv. Chem. Ser.* 133, 545 (1974).
14. Froment, G. F., *Ind. Eng. Chem.* 59, 18 (1967).
15. Von Rosenberg, D. U., "Methods for the Numerical Solution of Partial Differential Equations," Am. Elsevier, New York (1969).
16. Valstar, J. M., P. J. Van Den Berg, and J. Oyserman, *Chem. Eng. Sci.* 30, 723 (1975).
17. Finlayson, B. A., *Cat. Rev. Sci. Engr.* 10, 69 (1974).
18. Smith, T. G., *Chem. Eng. Sci.* 32, 1023 (1977).
19. Priestly, A. J. and J. B. Agnew, *Ind. Eng. Chem., Proc. Des. Dev.* 14, 171 (1975).
20. Barkelew, C. R., *CEP Symp. Ser.* 55 (25), 38 (1959).
21. Van Welsenaere, R. J. and G. F. Froment, *Chem. Eng. Sci.* 25, 1503 (1970).
22. McGreavy, C. and C. I. Adderley, *Chem. Eng. Sci.* 28, 577 (1973).
23. Schleppy, R., Jr., and Y. T. Shah, *Chem. Eng. Sci.* 32, 881 (1977).
24. Luss, D. and N. R. Amundson, *Chem. Eng. Sci.* 22, 253 (1967).
25. Hlavacek, V. and H. Hofmann, *Chem. Eng. Sci.* 25, 173 (1970).
26. Hlavacek, V. and H. Hofmann, *Chem. Eng. Sci.* 25, 187 (1970).

SUGGESTED COMPLEMENTARY READING

1. Froment, G. F., "Fixed Bed Catalytic Reactors Technological and Fundamental Design Aspects," *Chem.-Ing.-Tech.* 46, 374 (1974).
2. Hlavacek, V. and J. Votruba, "Steady-State Operation of Fixed-Bed Reactors and Monolithic Structures," in "Chemical Reactor Theory. A Review, Lapidus," L. and N. R. Amundson, eds., Prentice-Hall, Englewood Cliffs, New Jersey (1977).
3. Young, L. C. and B. A. Finlayson, "Axial Dispersion in Non-isothermal Packed Bed Chemical Reactors," *Ind. Eng. Chem., Fund.* 12, 412 (1973).

STUDY PROBLEMS

1. Define all terms which appear in Equations 1 and 2.

2. List all assumptions which form the basis of Equations 1 and 2 and comment on the validity of each.

3. How many dimensionless parameters figure into the design of a packed bed reactor under the assumptions of Table 1?

4. Discuss the importance of axial dispersion in the design of packed bed reactors.

5. The mass and energy balances for an adiabatic reactor are given by Equations 36 and 37 with appropriate boundary conditions. Under what circumstances can one of these differential equations be replaced with a simple algebraic relation?

6. What boundary conditions are appropriate for use with Equations 47 and 48?

7. What boundary conditions are appropriate for use with Equations 7 and 8?

8. A student carries out a computer simulation of a NANIR and finds that his program becomes numerically unstable for a certain range of parameter values, i.e. the computation is plagued by "underflow" or "overflow" messages. Is there a possible explanation (other than the trivial explanation—programming errors)?

HOMEWORK PROBLEMS

1. Consider an isothermal packed bed reactor divided into a fore section (a), a catalyst bed section (b), and an aft section (c) as illustrated in the figure(5):

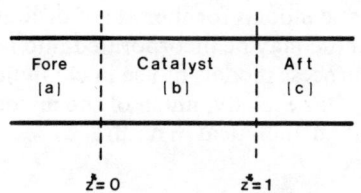

The fore and aft sections contain no catalyst. Upon writing Equation 25 for each zone, one obtains:

$$\frac{1}{N_{Pe_a}} \frac{d^2X}{dz^{*2}} - \frac{dX}{dz^*} = 0 \quad \text{where} \quad -\infty < z^* < 0 \tag{1.1}$$

$$\frac{1}{N_{Pe}} \frac{d^2X}{dz^{*2}} - \frac{dX}{dz^*} - R^* = 0 \quad \text{where} \quad 0 < z^* < 1 \tag{1.2}$$

$$\frac{1}{N_{Pe_c}} \frac{d^2X}{dz^{*2}} - \frac{dX}{dz^*} = 0 \quad \text{where} \quad 1 < z^* < \infty \tag{1.3}$$

An appropriate set of boundary conditions is:

$$X(-\infty) = 0 \tag{1.4}$$

$$X(0^-) - \frac{1}{N_{Pe_a}} \frac{dX}{dz^*}(0^-) = X(0^+) - \frac{1}{N_{Pe}} \frac{dX}{dz^*}(0^+) \tag{1.5}$$

$$X(0^-) = X(0^+) \tag{1.6}$$

$$X(1^-) - \frac{1}{N_{Pe}} \frac{dX}{dz^*}(1^-) = X(1^+) - \frac{1}{N_{Pe_c}} \frac{dX}{dz^*}(1^+) \tag{1.7}$$

$$X(1^-) = X(1^+) \tag{1.8}$$

$$X(\infty) = \text{finite} \tag{1.9}$$

The boundary conditions at $z^* = 0$ and $z^* = 1$ insure continuity of concentrations (or conversions) at the bed inlet and outlet as well as conservation of reactant taking into account flow and dispersion.

Show that this system of equations is equivalent to Equations 25 to 27 of the text. Is it necessary to make any assumptions regarding the nature of dispersion in the fore and aft sections in order to obtain this result?

2. Consider an axially dispersed adiabatic packed bed reactor in which the gas phase reaction $A \rightarrow B$ takes place. While no change in moles with conversion is of concern, the density does vary due to the varying temperature within the reactor. Assume that the variation in density is in accord with the ideal gas law and that pressure is uniform. Thus:

$$\rho = \rho_0 \left(\frac{T_0}{T}\right)$$

$$u = u_0 \left(\frac{T}{T_0}\right)$$

Assume that the temperature dependencies of the fluid phase heat capacity and heat of reaction are small and can be neglected for our purposes. However, it is desirable to take into account the temperature dependencies of the axial dispersion coefficients. The reactor is operating under conditions such that $N_{Re_p} > 10$ and it can be reasonably assumed that the heat and mass transfer Peclet numbers are equal. Neglect inter- and intraparticle heat and mass transfer effects.

a) Under these conditions, show that the reactant mass balance is given by:

$$\frac{1}{N_{Pe}^0} \frac{d}{dz^*}\left(T^* \frac{dC^*}{dz^*}\right) - \frac{d}{dz^*}(T^*C^*) + R^* = 0$$

Where $C^* = C_A/C_{AO}$ = reduced concentration (Note: The equations are a bit less cumbersome when written in terms of C^*, as compared with the alternative formulation in terms of X).

b) Show that the appropriate differential energy balance is:

$$\frac{1}{N_{Pe}^0} \frac{d^2T^*}{dz^{*2}} - \frac{dT^*}{dz^*} + \Delta H^* R^* = 0$$

Where N_{Pe}^0 and R^* are based on the inlet density, i.e.

$$N_{Pe}^0 = \frac{u_0 L}{D_{zO}} = \frac{u_0 \rho_0 C_p L}{\lambda_{zO}}$$

and

$$R^* = \frac{L \rho_b R_{AW}}{u_0 C_{AO}}$$

Otherwise, the notation is identical to that in the text of the module.

c) Derive the appropriate boundary conditions applicable to this problem.

3. Write a computer program for solving the one-dimensional packed bed reactor equations, Equations 43 and 44. Assume that only one reaction takes place. Test your program using the parameter values of Figure 3.

Catalyst Deactivation: Mechanisms and Kinetics

John B. Butt

Department of Chemical Engineering
Northwestern University
Evanston, Illinois 60201

OBJECTIVES
Upon completion of this module, the student should be able to:
1. Understand some of the basic mechanisms and kinetic models for catalyst deactivation.
2. Formulate kinetic descriptions for catalyst deactivation.
3. Understand the distinctions among poisoning, coke formation and sintering.
4. Distinguish between deactivation effects on activity and selectivity.
5. Describe both separable and nonseparable deactivation mechanisms.

PREREQUISITE MATHEMATICAL SKILLS
1. Ordinary differential equation solving.

PREREQUISITE ENGINEERING AND SCIENCE SKILLS
1. Chemical kinetics, including heterogeneous catalysis.

The rate of reactions on surfaces differs from many rates characteristic of homogeneous systems, in that they tend to change with chronological time. The reason for this is normally because some process is occurring simultaneously with the catalytic reaction to diminish the ability of the surface to catalyze the given reaction. Generally this behavior is termed deactivation, and it can be the result of several distinct types of microscopic phenomena. Deactivation can be of profound importance in the proper analysis or design of a catalytic process, since catalyst life may dictate the ultimate economics involved, or alterations in selectivity via deactivation may render a potentially attractive process completely infeasible.

Our purpose here is to determine what some of the microscopic processes—both physical and chemical—are which lead to deactivation, to examine possible rational kinetic models for the rate of deactivation, and to see how these may be incorporated into larger scale reaction or process models of use in catalytic reaction engineering. Of necessity, much of the material is more descriptive than analytical in nature.

POSSIBLE KINETIC MODELS FOR DEACTIVATION

The task of the kineticist dealing with measurements of reaction rates on deactivating catalysts is indeed formidable. Under those conditions, the activity (and other properties) of the catalyst is a function of its entire history, including preparation, handling, storage, pretreatment and specific deactivation mechanisms. When this reaction rate functional can be expressed as the product of two terms, reaction kinetic dependencies which are time independent and activity dependencies which are not, the overall kinetics are termed separable and two equations are used to express the reaction rate behavior. The rate of the main reaction at any time, r_T, is given by:

$$(-r_T) = r_1(C) \cdot r_2(T) \cdot r_3(s) \qquad (1)$$

where $r_1(C)$, $r_2(T)$ are concentrations and temperature dependent terms, characteristic of the reaction in the absence of deactivation, and $r_3(s)$ is a separable factor expressing the current activity of the catalyst with reference to some standard condition. The kinetics of deactivation are expressed in a second equation:

$$(-r_s) = r_4(C) \cdot r_5(T) \cdot r_6(s) \qquad (2)$$

where $(-r_s)$ is the rate of change in activity, $r_4(C)$ and $r_5(T)$ concentration and temperature factors pertaining to the deactivation kinetics, and $r_6(s)$ a factor reflecting the fact that the rate of change of activity is often proportional to the activity. Now, very often in practice the separable factor $r_3(s)$ is taken to be a normalized variable, s, with $0 \leq s \leq 1$, where $s = 1$ would reflect the fresh catalytic surface and $s = 0$ the totally deactivated catalytic surface. Similarly, $r_6(s)$ is often represented by the separable factor s.

Example 1:
Apply the concept of separable deactivation kinetics

to an isomerization reaction $A \to B$ being carried out on an ideal surface where Langmuir-Hinshelwood kinetics apply. The activity of the surface is uniform at s, with $0 \leq s \leq 1$.

We may write the elementary steps of this reaction as:

$$A(g) + * \rightleftarrows A(\text{ads}) \qquad (k_1, k_2)$$
$$A(\text{ads}) \to B(\text{ads}) \qquad (k_r)$$
$$B(\text{ads}) \rightleftarrows B(g) + * \qquad (k_3, k_4) \qquad \text{(I)}$$

where * is the isomerization active site and (ads) indicates adsorption. The kinetics of the three steps of (I) are:

$$k_1 s P_A (1 - \theta_A - \theta_B) = k_2 s \theta_A \qquad (3)$$

$$(-r_T) = k_r s \theta_A \qquad (4)$$

$$k_3 s \theta_B = k_4 s P_B (1 - \theta_A - \theta_B) \qquad (5)$$

and

$$\theta_A + \theta_B + \theta_v = 1 \qquad (6)$$

Here P_A and P_B are partial pressures of A and B, θ_A and θ_B the fraction of surface occupied by A and B, s the current level of activity of the surface, and θ_v the fraction of surface that is vacant.

In the normal procedure for obtaining an equation for $(-r_T)$ in terms of observable quantities, we eliminate θ_v via use of the equilibrium relationships in Equations 3 and 5 to obtain an expression for θ_A in terms of P_A, P_B, and $k_1 - k_4$. Clearly the net adsorption-desorption constants for the deactivated surface, $k_i s$, always appear in ratio, so that the activity variable divides out of the isotherm expression. The result for the overall reaction is then:

$$(-r_T) = \frac{k_r s K_A P_A}{(1 + K_A P_A + K_B P_B)} \qquad (7)$$

where $K_A = k_2/k_1$, etc. In this result, then:

$$r_1(C) \cdot r_2(T) = \frac{k_r K_A P_A}{(1 + K_A P_A + K_B P_B)} \qquad (8)$$

and

$$r_3(s) = s \qquad (9)$$

This example establishes a typical format for the application of Equation 1, but has little to say about how the surface has arrived at the activity value, $s \leq 1$. To properly address this problem, one needs to know something about (ds/dt); that is, something about the form of Equation 2. To do this, it is necessary to know more about detailed mechanisms of deactivation.

TYPICAL MECHANISMS OF DEACTIVATION

In general, one can identify three principal ways in which catalysts deactivate. These are:

1. Poisoning; in which the loss of activity is caused by strong chemisorption of some impurity normally contained in the reaction mixture.
2. Coking or Fouling; in which the loss of activity is caused by reactant or product degradation on the surface. As the name implies, this is associated mostly with hydrocarbon reactions via the formation of carbonaceous residues on the surface.
3. Sintering; in which the loss of activity is caused by a decrease in active surface area.

The first two of these mechanisms are clearly chemical in nature, and because it is possible in many cases to identify the specific chemical nature of the poisons and the active sites involved, particularly elegant studies of impurity poisoning have been carried out. Coke formation is not so readily analyzed in detail, since the nature of the processes where this is important, involves in many cases, multicomponent reactants (i.e., refinery feedstocks) and many reaction pathways for deactivation. Sintering is normally thought of as a physical process, thermally activated, but in kinetic description should not differ greatly from the chemical mechanisms. This module will present examples from the literature which illustrate possible kinetic correlations for these mechanisms; it is understood that these are representative and illustrative, not comprehensive.

Poisoning

Since poisoning is said to be due to strong chemisorption, it is reasonable to look at some examples of strong adsorption on surfaces as candidates. The chemisorption of various organic sulfur compounds on catalytic metals, such as Pt or Ni, is one case; while the chemisorption of basic organic molecules, such as pyridene on oxides such as Al_2O_3, is a second. In Table 1, three examples are given of studies reporting on these systems, entries 1–3. Of particular interest for an analysis of possible kinetic correlations, is the listing under "Activity-time." Here, both linear and exponential correlations are reported, indicative of zero- or first-order kinetics. Since the strong chemisorption of poison occurs in parallel with the main reaction, it seems reasonable that a plausible kinetic scheme for this type of deactivation would be given by:

$$A + S \to B + S \qquad \text{(main reaction)}$$
$$L + S \to L \cdot S \qquad \text{(poisoning reaction)} \qquad \text{(II)}$$

where L is the poison and S the surface site. The kinetics of deactivation may be written from (II) as:

$$(-r_s) = -\frac{ds}{dt} = k_d C_L^n s \qquad (10)$$

where s is proportional to the concentration of active sites, k_d is a deactivation rate constant, and $n = 0$ or 1, in accord with experimental observation.

Example 2:

Derive the expression for the rate of reaction as a function of time of operation for (II), assuming that order corresponds to stoichiometry ($n = 1$).

Since $n = 1$, Equation 10 will apply directly in the form:

$$\frac{ds}{dt} = -k_d C_L s \qquad (11)$$

Table 1. Examples of catalyst deactivation [References (1)-(7)]

System	Activity-time	Comments
Poisoning of Pt, hydrogenation, by metals, S, N cds. (1)	linear, exponential	First systematic investigation of impurity poisoning effects on noble metals
Poisoning of SiO_2 and SiO_2/Al_2O_3 by organic bases, cracking reactions (2)	exponential	Demonstrated acidic nature of these oxides, developed activity correlation based on poisoning behavior
Poisoning of different types of Al_2O_3 with various alkali metals, isomerization and dehydration reactions (3)	linear, exponential	Showed specificity of poisoning behavior to both chemical nature of poison and reaction
Coking of metal oxide cracking catalysts (4)	power law, time on stream	Developed correlation for coke on catalyst vs. time of reaction
Coking of SiO_2/Al_2O_3 and zeolite cracking catalysts (5)	exponential, time on stream	Deactivation and kinetic models for catalytic cracking
Sintering in reforming on Pt/Al_2O_3 (6)	hyperbolic	Preferential deactivation of one function of a bifunctional catalyst
Sintering, primarily supported Pt (7)	many	Review paper

On integration,

$$\int_1^s \frac{ds}{s} = -k_d C_L t = \ln s$$

$$s = e^{-k_d C_L t} \quad (12)$$

The rate of the main reaction is thus:

$$(-r_T) = k_T e^{-k_d C_L t} C_A \quad (13)$$

Further, consider now the conversion in the main reaction in a batch reactor:

$$\int_{C_{A_0}}^{C_A} \frac{dC_A}{C_A} = -\int_0^t k_T e^{-k_d C_L t} dt \quad (14)$$

so:

$$\ln\left(\frac{C_A}{C_{A_0}}\right) = \ln(1-x) = \frac{k_T e^{-k_d C_L t}}{k_d C_L} - \frac{k_T}{k_d C_L} \quad (15)$$

Note that this requires $C_L \neq f(t)$, which may not be the case.

Coking

As mentioned previously, coking is often associated with the catalytic reactions of complex hydrocarbon mixtures and is therefore not easily resolved, mechanistically. Generally speaking, the tendency for coke formation increases with the degree of unsaturation and molecular size; polycyclic aromatic compounds, such as anthracene, are particularly strong coke formers. Owing to this difficulty in identification of specific mechanisms, the major history in the literature has been one of developing "time on stream" correlations, shown in entries 4 and 5 of Table 1. One will also note there that the correlations relate the amount of coke on catalyst to time, not activity directly. Hence one must normally establish a second correlation relating catalyst activity to time on stream. The correlation of Voorhies proposed that:

$$C_c = a t_c^m \quad (16)$$

where C_c is weight of coke on catalyst, t_c time on stream, and a and m empirical constants. An extended series of studies on coking in catalytic cracking has established a reciprocal power law to be a good representation of the second correlation required, that between activity and coke content. Thus:

$$s = 1/C_c^p \quad (17)$$

Combining this with Equation 16 it becomes:

$$s = 1/t_c^w \quad (18)$$

where $w = p \cdot m$. In practice, this can be closely approximated by an exponential function:

$$s = e^{-\alpha t_c} \quad (19)$$

where α is some characteristic coking constant (entry 5, Table 1).

The similarity of Equation 19 for coking to Equation 12 for poisoning strongly suggests that a kinetic scheme might be written for coke deposition, in a manner analogous to scheme (II) but keeping in mind that it is the reactants or products that are responsible for deactivation, not some independent agent. In the simplest case, two limits—reactant or product coking—can be envisioned:

$$A + S \rightarrow B + S$$
$$A + S \rightarrow A \cdot S \quad \text{(IIIa)}$$

or:

$$A + S \rightarrow B + S$$
$$B + S \rightarrow B \cdot S \quad \text{(IIIb)}$$

The appropriate kinetic model, using (IIIa) as an example, is:

$$(-r_T) = k_T C_A s \quad (20)$$

$$(-r_s) = -\frac{ds}{dt} = k_d C_A s \quad (21)$$

where α of Equation 19 is identified with $k_d C_A$ of

Equation 21, and the integration of Equation 21 is carried out from 0 to t_c.

Sintering

The agglomeration of small metal crystallites into larger ones, which is the process involved in the important case of sintering deactivation of supported metal catalysts, is a physical phenomenon which is not at all well understood. Clearly the activity of the catalyst will be related to surface area, but beyond this one must resort to literature correlations for kinetic models. One possible scheme might be:

$$A + S \rightarrow B + S$$
$$S + S \rightarrow S \cdot S \tag{IV}$$

in which the second step represents the physical sintering step, and a relation is set between the number of active sites S and activity variable s to the surface area. Hence:

$$(-r_T) = k_T C_A C_s \tag{22}$$

and

$$(-r_s) = -\frac{dC_s}{dt} = k_d C_s^2 \tag{23}$$

Since C_s is directly proportional to s,

$$(-r_T) = k_T C_A s \tag{22a}$$

$$(-r_s) = -\frac{ds}{dt} = k_d s^2 \tag{23a}$$

Equation 23a is one example of a large number of power-law correlations for sintering kinetics which have been reported in the literature (entries 6 and 7, Table 1). The adequacy of this approach, however, is open to serious doubt, since values of the exponent in Equation 23a ranging from 2 to 15 have been reported by various workers for very similar catalysts (supported Pt), with corresponding activation energies from 10 to 90 kcal/mol. Power law correlations of sintering kinetics must then be regarded as empirical for the most part; better understanding of this must await improved knowledge concerning the microscopic mechanisms involved in the migration and agglomeration of particles on surfaces.

ABOUT BIFUNCTIONAL CATALYSTS

An important class of industrial catalysts are those which possess two (or more) catalytic functions on the surface. One example is the isomerization of a normal paraffin, say n-pentane, on a Pt/Al$_2$O$_3$ catalyst. In this reaction, both the Pt and the Al$_2$O$_3$ have catalytic roles to perform. An accepted mechanism for this reaction is:

$$n - C_5 \xrightarrow[-H_2]{Pt} n - C_5^=$$
$$n - C_5^= \xrightarrow{Al_2O_3} i - C_5^=$$
$$i - C_5^= \xrightarrow[+H_2]{Pt} i - C_5 \tag{IV}$$

Here we see that the isomerization occurs on the acidic sites of the Al$_2$O$_3$ via an olefinic intermediate; the Pt is necessary to produce the reactive intermediate (the n-paraffin is nonreactive on Al$_2$O$_3$) via dehydrogenation, and to produce the iso-paraffin via hydrogenation of the iso-olefin. Other types of bifunctional reactions may also be envisioned. For the parallel hydroisomerization of an olefin, again using the C_5-Pt/Al$_2$O$_3$ system as an example:

$$n - C_5^= \xrightarrow[+H_2]{Pt} n - C_5$$
$$n - C_5^= \xrightarrow{Al_2O_3} i - C_5^=$$
$$(i - C_5^= \text{ may also hydrogenate}) \tag{V}$$

Reaction schemes (IV) and (V) differ in that the steps of (IV) occur in sequence while those of (V) are in parallel.

What are the implications of deactivation with respect to the utilization of these types of catalysts? The prime factor here has to do with selectivity, while the prior discussion was exclusively concerned with the variation of activity and its correlation in terms of kinetic models. Suppose, for example, that sintering of the Pt but not the Al$_2$O$_3$ is occurring in (V). Obviously this will have some effect on the overall rate of reaction of $n - C_5^=$, but there will be an even more pronounced effect on the selectivity of the catalyst between $n - C_5$ and $i - C_5^=$ products. A nice example of such selective deactivation is provided by entry 6 in Table 1. Reaction networks for the deactivation of bifunctional catalysts can be written in much the same way as for the monofunctional cases. For illustration, consider the poisoning of a bifunctional catalyst with one reaction being carried out on the X function and a parallel reaction on the Y function. These two functions are independently poisoned by the molecules L and M:

Main Reactions:

$$A + S_1 \xrightarrow{X} B + S_1$$
$$C + S_2 \xrightarrow{Y} D + S_2$$

Poisoning

$$L + S_1 \xrightarrow{X} L \cdot S_1$$
$$M + S_2 \xrightarrow{Y} M \cdot S_2 \tag{VI}$$

A point or differential selectivity is defined according to this scheme, as:

$$\frac{(-r_{TA})}{(-r_{TC})} = \frac{k_{T1} C_A s_1}{k_{T2} C_C s_2} \tag{24}$$

and:

$$\frac{ds_1}{dt} = -k_{d1} C_L s_1 \tag{25}$$

$$\frac{ds_2}{dt} = -k_{d2} C_M s_2 \tag{26}$$

Example 3:

Obtain an expression for the point selectivity as a function of time for the bifunctional scheme (VI).

From integration of Equations 25 and 26

$$\ln s_1 = -k_{d1} C_L t$$

$$\ln s_2 = -k_{d2}C_M t$$

Thus:

$$\frac{(-r_{TA})}{(-r_{TC})} = \frac{k_{T1}C_A e^{-k_{d1}C_L t}}{k_{T2}C_C e^{-k_{d2}C_M t}} = S_P(\text{VI}) \tag{27}$$

Equation 27 may be rearranged to the form:

$$\ln [S_P(\text{VI})] = (k_{d2}C_M - k_{d1}C_L)t + \ln \alpha \tag{28}$$

with

$$\alpha = \frac{k_{T1}C_A}{k_{T2}C_C}$$

Now, by obtaining experimental data on $S_P(\text{VI})$ at different temperature levels, the values of k_{d1} and k_{d2} may be obtained from the shapes and intercepts of the indicated linear plot of $\ln [S_P(\text{VI})]$ versus t.

VALIDITY OF THE SEPARABLE REPRESENTATION

Example 1 demonstrated the application of the separable model for deactivation kinetics to a simple isomerization reaction on an ideal surface. It is reasonable to ask just how general this approach is, in view of the fact that most reactions are more complicated than isomerizations and most surfaces are not ideal. Consider the problem of non-ideal surfaces. One may assume that such a surface consists of an assembly of subunits, each of which acts as an ideal surface, but distributed with respect to some property of the overall surface which is measurable. The heat of chemisorption of reactant is often a convenient quantity to use as a distribution variable, so for a subunit of the surface characterized by heat of chemisorption q the rate of the isomerization is:

$$r_q = \frac{s_q k_q K_q P}{1 + K_q P} \tag{29}$$

and the overall rate of reaction is obtained by summation over the n individual subsurfaces:

$$(-r_T) = \sum_n n_q r_q = \int_0^{q_m} n_q r_q \, dq \tag{30}$$

where q_m is the maximum heat of chemisorption. Inserting the kinetics:

$$(-r)_T = \int_0^{q_m} \frac{n_q s_q k_q K_q P}{1 + K_q P} \, dq \tag{31}$$

with:

$$K_q = K_0 e^{q/RT}$$

$$k_q = k_0 e^{-E/RT}$$

Normally the activation energy E can be approximated as some function of q; a form often used is simply $E = -\beta q$. In order to solve the problem, the nature of the distributions n_q and s_q must be specified. The corresponding separable formulation for the non-ideal surface is:

$$(-r_T)_S = \langle s \rangle \int_0^{q_m} \frac{n_q k_q K_q P}{(1 + K_q P)} \, dq \tag{32}$$

with:

$$\langle s \rangle = \frac{\int_0^{q_m} s_q \, dq}{q_m} \tag{33}$$

It is apparent that the integrations of Equation 31 and 33 will in general not result in the same overall functionality, so the assumption of separability is an approximation that must be treated carefully in model extrapolation.

NOMENCLATURE

a	—empirical parameter in correlation of Equation 16
C	—concentration
C_A, C_{A_0}	—concentration of reactant A, C_{A_0} is initial value
C_c	—weight percent coke on catalyst
C_L, C_M	—poison concentrations
C_s	—pseudo concentration variable related to surface area
E	—activation energy
k_0	—pre-exponential factor for k_q
k_q	—rate of reaction associated with heat of chemisorption q
k_r	—surface reaction rate constant
k_T, k_d	—rate constants for main and deactivation reactions, respectively
k_{T1}, k_{T2}	—rate constants for main reaction in bifunctional scheme
k_{d1}, k_{d2}	—deactivation rate constants for functions X and Y
k_1, k_2, k_3, k_4	—adsorption-desorption rate constants, reaction scheme (I)
K_A, K_B	—adsorption equilibrium constants
K_0	—pre-exponential factor for K_q
K_q	—adsorption equilibrium constant for sites with heat of chemisorption q
m	—empirical parameter in correlation of Equation 16
n	—power dependence of deactivation on poison
n_q	—number of sites associated with heat of chemisorption q
p	—empirical parameter in Equation 17
P	—total pressure
P_A, P_B	—partial pressures of A and B
q	—heat of chemisorption
q_m	—maximum heat of chemisorption
$r_1(C), r_2(T), r_3(s)$	—concentration, temperature and activity factors for main reaction
$r_4(C), r_5(T), r_6(s)$	—concentration, temperature and activity factors for deactivation reaction
$(-r_s)$	—rate of change in activity
$(-r_T)$	—rate of the main reaction
r_q	—rate of reaction associated with sites of heat of chemisorption q

$(-r_{TA})$, $(-r_{TC})$	—overall rates for A and C on a bifunctional catalyst
$(-r_T)_S$	—main reaction rate with separable kinetics assumption
R	—gas constant
s	—activity variable
s_q	—activity associated with heat of chemisorption q
s_1, s_2	—activity variables for functions X and Y
S	—surface site; as subscript referring to separable
$S_p(VI)$	—bifunctional selectivity, defined in Equation 27
t	—time
t_c	—time on stream
T	—temperature
w	—defined as $p \cdot m$
X, Y	—functions in a bifunctional catalyst
α	—characteristic coking constant, Equation 19, or parameter of Equation 28
β	—characterization constant in $E = -\beta q$
$\theta_A, \theta_B, \theta_v$	—fraction of sites occupied (A, B) and vacant (v)

LITERATURE CITED

1. Maxted, E. B., *Adv. Catalysis*, 3, 129 (1951).
2. Mills, G. A., E. R. Boedeker and A. G. Oblad, *J. Am. Chem. Soc.*, 72, 1554 (1950).
3. Pines, H. and W. O. Haag, *J. Am. Chem. Soc.*, 82, 2471 (1960).
4. Voorhies, A., Jr., *Ind. Eng. Chem.*, 37, 318 (1945).
5. Weekman, V. W., Jr., *Ind. Eng. Chem. Proc. Design Devel.*, 7, 90 (1968); 8, 388 (1969); Weekman, Jr., V. W., and D. M. Nace, *AIChE J.*, 16, 397 (1970); Nace, D. M., S. E. Voltz, and V. W. Weekman, Jr., *Ind. Eng. Chem. Proc. Design Devel.*, 10, 530, 538 (1971).
6. Maat, H. J. and L. Moscou, "Proc. Int. Cong. on Catalysis," 3rd ed., p. 1277, North Holland, Amsterdam (1965).
7. Wanke, S. E. and P. C. Flynn, *Cat. Rev.—Sci. and Engr.*, 12, 93 (1975).

Note: A fairly comprehensive review of the literature on catalyst deactivation by the author, current through 1971, appeared in *Advances in Chemistry*, 109, 259, (1972). See also Proceedings of the Fifth International Symposium on Chemical Reaction Engineering, Houston, ACS Symposium Series (1978).

STUDY PROBLEMS

1. The ideal surface definition involved in the application of separable kinetics requires an energetically homogeneous surface. What does this mean as far as chemisorption on such a surface is concerned?

2. What might be some possible mechanisms for catalyst deactivation in addition to those discussed here?

3. Pyridine is a strong poison for alumina surfaces. Would you expect the pyridinium ion to exhibit similar behavior? Why?

4. The regeneration of coked catalyst by oxygen is a process intimately connected with deactivation problems. Experimentally it is observed that the kinetics of coke burning are first-order in oxygen and zero order in coke. What would be a physical interpretation of the zero order dependency?

5. What individual steps might be involved in the sintering of a supported metal catalyst?

6. What would be the observed effect if only the Pt function were deactivated in (IV)? If only the Al_2O_3 function were deactivated?

HOMEWORK PROBLEMS

1. Propose a series of experiments and the consequent interpretation of data from which the kinetic parameters can be obtained for the results of Example 3. Comment upon a similar interpretation for Example 2.

2. Obtain the conversion-time relationship according to (IV) for second-order sintering in a batch reactor.

3. An hyperbolic form of time on stream correlation for coking has been proposed as:

$$s = \frac{1}{(1 + Gt_c)^M}$$

The rate model is:

$$\frac{ds}{dt} = -K_d s^n$$

a) What is the significance of G and M in terms of the kinetic model parameters?
b) Under what conditions might this form be essentially equivalent to the exponential time on stream model?

4. Compare the results of Equation 31 and 32 for the following site and activity distributions:

$$n_q = \frac{2n_o}{q_m} q \qquad (0 \leq q \leq q_m/2)$$

$$n_q = \frac{2n_o}{q_m}(q_m - q) \qquad (q_m/2 \leq q \leq q_m)$$

$$s_q = \left[\frac{s_m - s_o}{q_m}\right] q + s_o$$

You will find the general form of the result difficult to evaluate, so express your solution in terms of $(-r_T)/(-r_T)_S$ as evaluated for the low pressure limit, $K_q P \ll 1$. Parameter values are: $s_o = 0.8$, $s_m = 0.2$, $q_m = 25$ kcal/mol, $\beta = 0.75$, $T = 373$ K. All other parameters divide out in the ratio of rates.

Modular Instruction Series

APPENDIX

Solutions to the Study Problems

Solutions to the Homework Problems are available as a separate reprint from the AIChE Educational Services Dept., 345 East 47th St., New York, NY 10017.

SOLUTIONS TO THE STUDY PROBLEMS

1. From a comparison of Eqs. (2) and (5) it is evident that the measured effective diffusivity will respond differently to a small change in pressure depending upon the mode of diffusion. If the experimental effective diffusivity is not influenced by changes in pressure then Knudsen diffusion predominates. In the presence of a substantial ordinary diffusion contribution the measured effective diffusivity will decrease with increasing pressure. A similar analysis could be made on the basis of variations in temperature, but one should keep in mind the fact that the predictions of Eqs. (2) and (5) are only approximate with regard to temperature.

2. The effective diffusivity is not concentration dependent when mass transfer is by Knudsen diffusion. The assumption of constant effective diffusivity is approximately valid in the ordinary diffusion mode when volume change with reaction is small or when the reactant mole fraction is small as when reactant is diluted by product or inerts. Effective diffusivities are sometimes highly concentration dependent when surface diffusion or configurational diffusion is a factor.

3. The solution to this problem is best illustrated by considering a two dimensional example. Due to the random orientation of pores in two dimensions the path length actually followed by the diffusing molecules will be larger than the shortest path between two points by a factor $\sqrt{2}$. Letting z be the path in the direction of diffusion and ℓ be the path actually traversed, then $\ell = \sqrt{2}\, z$ and:

$$\frac{dC_A}{d\ell} = \frac{1}{\sqrt{2}} \frac{dC_A}{dz} \quad , \quad N_A^{(P)} = \sqrt{2}\, N_A$$

Thus:

$$N_A^{(P)} = D \frac{dC_A}{d\ell}$$

and

$$N_A = \frac{D}{2} \frac{dC_A}{dz}$$

In three dimensions the diffusion coefficient must be divided by a factor of three to account for tortuosity.

4. For a system of uniform pores the pore size distribution function is given by $f_v(r) = \delta(r-r_p)$ where r_p is the pore radius and δ is the unit impulse function. Thus:

$$\int_0^\infty D_{TA}(r) f_v(r) dr = \int_0^\infty D_{TA}(r) \delta(r-r_p) dr = D_{TA}(r_p)$$

and

$$D_A^e = \frac{\theta D_{TA}(r_p)}{3}$$

5. Since pressure is uniform in the Wicke-Kallenbach experiment Eq. (6) can be written in the form:

$$N_A = -\frac{C_T}{\frac{1}{D'_{KA}} + \frac{1-\alpha y_A}{D'_{AB}}} \frac{dy_A}{dz}$$

where the primes signify "effective" diffusivities. This expression is easily integrated over the pellet length to give:

$$N_A = \frac{C_T D'_{AB}}{\alpha L} \text{Ln} \left[\frac{1-\alpha y_{AL} + D'_{AB}/D'_{KA}}{1-\alpha y_{A0} + D'_{AB}/D'_{KA}} \right]$$

The principal reason why Eq. (6) has not seen widespread application to problems of diffusion and reaction in porous catalysts is the computational difficulties arising from a concentration dependent diffusivity.

6. Since the n-th moment contains terms involving t^n in the integrand, the higher moments are strongly influenced by a tailing response curve. In a practical situation instrument baseline drift may lead to fictitious tailing. Also, phenomena not considered in the model, e.g. a small number of high energy adsorption sites, may contribute to tailing. In either case the evaluation of higher moments is error prone.

7. The term containing D_y^e also contains the catalyst particle radius, R_y. By conducting experiments at two or more particle sizes the D_x^e and D_y^e terms can be separated.

American Institute of Chemical Engineers

Module E3.2

SOLUTIONS TO THE STUDY PROBLEMS

1. For large x we can make the approximations $\tanh(x) \cong 1$. Then from Eq. (13):

$$\eta = \frac{\tanh(h_x)}{h_x} \cong \frac{1}{h_x} = \frac{1}{h}\left(\frac{\ell_0}{x_0}\right) = \frac{1}{h}$$

Similarly Eq. (17) becomes for large h_s:

$$\eta = \frac{3}{h_s}\left[\frac{1}{\tanh(h_s)} - \frac{1}{h_s}\right] \cong \frac{3}{h_s}\left(1 - \frac{1}{h_s}\right)$$

$$\cong \frac{3}{h_s} = \frac{3}{h}\left(\frac{\ell_0}{r_0}\right) = \frac{3}{h}\left(\frac{1}{3}\right) = \frac{1}{h}$$

For large x we make use of the asymptotic relation $I_n(x) \cong e^x/\sqrt{2\pi x}$ which is valid for all n. Then $I_0(x) \cong I_1(x)$ and Eq. 18 becomes:

$$\eta = \frac{2I_1(H_c)}{h_c I_0(h_c)} \cong \frac{2}{h_c} = \frac{2}{h}\left(\frac{\ell_0}{r_0}\right) = \frac{2}{h}\left(\frac{1}{2}\right) = \frac{1}{h}$$

By substituting numerical values into these expressions it can be verified that the error in these approximations is below five percent for $h_x > 1.86$, $h_s > 21.0$, and $h_c > 10.8$.

2. The modulus h is convenient for use in reactor design problems when the intrinsic kinetics are known. The modulus Φ is convenient for use in the analysis of kinetics data since all quantities are observable. The generalized modulus, m, is useful for estimating the effectiveness factor for "normal" reactions (i.e. rate decreases with reactant concentration) when exact numerical solutions are not available.

Modular Instruction Series

3. It is apparent from Eq. (21) that the Thiele modulus is a ratio of the rate of reaction relative to the rate of intraparticle mass transfer. When this modulus is small, reaction is slow relative to diffusion and the system operates in a kinetics regime. When it is large, mass transfer is slow relative to reaction and the observed reaction is limited by mass transfer.

4. When reaction is extremely rapid so that the entire reaction takes place near the surface of the particle, calculations for all particle geometries are convergent to flat plate geometry.

5. Calculations based upon the generalized Thiele modulus will be in error for intermediate values of the Thiele modulus during situations in which the effectiveness factor can be greater than unity, i.e. nonisothermal exothermic reaction and/or negative reaction order with regard to reactant. The calculations are exact in the asymptotic limit corresponding to zero concentration at the center of the pellet and flat plate geometry, i.e. large Thiele modulus.

6. The rate must be based upon a unit volume of catalyst particle.

Module E3.3

SOLUTIONS TO THE STUDY PROBLEMS

1. We need the mass balance, the energy balance or Prater relation, the kinetics eqpression and the Arrhenius relation or other equations relating kinetics constants to temperature, i.e. Eqs (1), (5), (8) and the appropriate kinetics equation.

2. The effectiveness factory may be greater than unity when (1) the reaction order is negative with regard to reactant concentrations (i.e. rate increases with conversion) or when (2) the particle is nonisothermal and reaction is exothermic.

3. From Eq. (14) we see that pressure gradients will be significant unless (1) B_0 is large (i.e. the pore size is large since $B_0 \; r_p^2$) or (2) the stoichiometric flux ratin corresponds to

$$N_B + N_A \left(\frac{D_{KB}^e}{D_{KA}^e}\right) = 0$$

or $N_B/N_A = -\sqrt{M_A/M_B} = -\sqrt{\nu}$, since stoichiometry requires that $M_A/M_B = \nu$. Since stoichiometry also requires that $N_B/M_A = -\nu$ we see that a pressure gradient will generally exist in small pore catalysts except for the special case $\nu = 1$. This result is also valid for multicomponent systems as the student can verify from the equation

$$\sum_{i=1}^{n} \frac{N_i}{D_{Ki}^e} = -\frac{1}{RT}\left[1 + \frac{PB_0^e}{\mu} \sum_{i=1}^{n} \frac{y_i}{D_{Ki}^e}\right] \frac{dP}{dz}$$

which is a generalization of Eq. (14).

4. Hardly ever. As illustrated in Fig. 3 the pressure gradient in real systems ($\gamma\beta \tilde{=} 0.1$, see Homework Problem 2) is closely approximated by Eq. (31) which neglects the viscous flow term.

Note that even though viscous transport can be neglected, substantial pressure gradients can exist.

5. Equations (49) and (50) relate component i concentrations to the key reactant concentration for all kinetics expressions and particle geometries. Equation (5) similarly relates temperature to the key reactant concentration.

6. The effectiveness factor can be estimated from the relation

$$\eta \cong \frac{\tanh(m)}{m}$$

providing that the reaction is normal and the pellet is isothermal (or nonisothermal-endothermic). Otherwise this approach is valid only in the asymptotic limit, i.e. large m.

SOLUTIONS TO THE STUDY PROBLEMS

1. $$\eta = \frac{R_{obs}}{R(C_S, T_S)} \qquad \eta' = \frac{R_{obs}}{R(C_B, T_B)}$$

    In reactor design problems the bulk fluid conditions in the vicinity of the pellet are known, hence $R(C_B, T_B)$ is readily calculated and the actual reaction rate, R_{obs}, is obtained using the effectiveness factor, η'. Numerical computations of the effectiveness factor, η, are available for many systems, but because of the increased number of parameters in η' relatively few computations have been carried out. For symmetrical particles the two effectiveness factors are related by the equations in Table I (or similar equations for non power law kinetics).

2. Intraparticle mass transfer can only limit the rate of reaction. The rate will depend upon the intrinsic activity even in the asymptotic limit of strong intraparticle diffusion limitations---see Eqs. (33) and (34) of module E3.2. Interparticle mass transfer can control the reaction, however. In the limit of infinite reaction rate in a spherical catalyst particle it follows from Eq. (1) that $-R_{obs} = (3k_c/r_0) C_{AB}$. The reaction is uninfluenced by intrinsic activity.

3. It is evident from the definition, Eqs. (7) and (8), that the Biot numbers are a measure of the relative rates of interphase transport to intraphase transport. Since convective heat and mass transfer coefficients tend to increase with increasing Reynolds number (which is in turn proportional to particle size), it is clear that external heat and mass transfer resistances tend to lose significance in comparison to intraparticle resistances as particle size increases.

4. Bulk fluid quantities and kinetics parameters (e.g. n, k_B, $\beta', \gamma', h', N_{Bi,m}$ and $N_{Bi,h}$) are known in a typical design problem. The unknown quantities are $T_S, C_{AS}, k_S, h, \beta, \gamma, \eta$ and η'. A convenient method of solution might be the following:

    a) Assume a value of T_S.

    b) Calculate the corresponding value of C_{AS} from

$$\frac{C_{AS}}{C_{AB}} = 1 - \frac{N_{Bi,h}}{\beta' N_{Bi,m}} \left(\frac{T_S}{T_B} - 1\right)$$

which is obtained by equating the left hand sides of Eqs. (19) and (22).

c) Calculate k_S, β, γ, and h from Eqs. (25), (24), (27), and (21) respectively.

d) Solve Eq. (15) for η.

e) Calculate T_S from Eq. (22) and compare with the assumed value.

f) If the assumed value is in error then assume another value of T_S (regula-falsi or some other iterative scheme may be helpful) and repeat steps (b) through (e).

g) Otherwise calculate η' from Eq. (18).

5. The two sets of boundary conditions will give identical results when the particle is symmetrical and bathed in a fluid of uniform concentration and temperature. See homework problem no. 2.

SOLUTIONS TO THE STUDY PROBLEMS

1. In small diameter packed beds ($d_t/d_p < 30$) radial velocity gradients become significant and the correlations for transport parameters in large diameter beds should not be applied. Not only are the transport coefficients different from those calculated for the correlations, but they may vary with position in the bed.

2. Since fluid flows in the axial direction only, the dispersion of mass and heat are different in the radial and axial directions. At low flow rates, as $N_{Re,p} \to 0$ one would expect the bed to behave isotropically and this is observed experimentally.

3. There is no reason why they should be the same since the Peclet No. depends upon the Reynolds No. and the Schmidt No.

4. There are no mass transfer analogies to heat transfer by solid conduction and radiation.

5. (1) Conduction through fluid, (2) conduction through solid, (3) conduction at point contacts, (4) conduction through fluid near point contacts, (5) convective heat transfer between solid and fluid, (6) heat transfer by lateral mixing of fluid, (7) radiation between particles, (8) radiation between voids.

6. The experimental technique normally used to evaluate the wall heat transfer coefficient is very insensitive to values of this parameter.

7. The question under debate is whether or not a limiting value of the Sherwood No. (or Nusselt No.) is applicable to packed beds. Some have argued quite convincingly that reported values of $N_{Sh} \ll 1$ are a consequence of failure to properly take into account axial dispersion in the data analysis.

SOLUTIONS TO THE STUDY PROBLEMS

1. All terms are defined in the notation. However, it should be emphasized that u = superficial velocity and the dispersion coefficients are defined according to

   $$N_z = -D_z \frac{\partial C_A}{\partial z}$$

   and

   $$q_z = -\lambda_z \frac{\partial C_A}{\partial z}$$

   where N_z and q_z are reactant and energy fluxes respectively per unit area of bed.

2. See Table 1.

3. A total of fourteen are listed in Table 2. If the wall temperature is different from the inlet temperature then we also have $T_w^* = T_w/T_0$.

4. Axial dispersion is unimportant in isothermal reactors with the possible exception of short laboratory reactors. Axial dispersion can also be neglected in most adiabatic reactors of industrial importance. In the design of nonadiabatic nonisothermal reactors, however, the contribution due to axial dispersion can be significant especially if the reactor operates near a region of parametric sensitivity.

5. When the mass and heat transfer Peclet numbers are equal, one can show that the relation

   $$T^* - 1 = -\Delta H^* X$$

is valid at any position within the reactor. Thus Eq. (37) can be eliminated from the computation.

6. Eqs. (17) to (20) and the initial conditions, $X(0) = 0$, $T^*(0) = 1$. It would be incorrect to use a curved inlet temperature profile in the computation even through such may be observed experimentally.

7. Eqs. (17) to (24). Actually Eqs. (21) to (24) are approximations to the exact boundary conditions. For the exact boundary conditions the student should consult ref. (4).

8. When the computer solution "blows up" it could well mean that the reactor will "blow up". The parametric sensitivity illustrated in Fig. 4 is not uncommon in highly exothermic and irreversible reactions, e.g. oxidations.

SOLUTIONS TO THE STUDY PROBLEMS

1. In order for a surface to remain energetically homogeneous on chemisorption there must be:

    a) A uniform site energy on the bare surface

    b) No distortion of this distribution as the surface becomes covered.

    Item b) is normally further refined to state that there are no interations between chemisorbed molecules, that adsorption ceases on formation of a monolayer, and that the probability of occupancy of a given site is unaffected by the occupancy or vacancy of sites surrounding.

2. a) Loss of active catalytic component via volatilization. Ruthenium was a promising candidate for NO_x control in automotive exhaust converters; however the oxides RuO_3 and RuO_4 were formed under certain conditions of operation. These materials are relatively volatile under the conditions of converter operation and the original Ru loading disappeared after short periods of operation.

    b) Physical coating of active surface. This was cited as one way in which coke can deactivate a surface. Trace metals deposition (Ni and V particularly) from organometallic components in hydrotreating feedstacks and lead deposition on auto exhaust converters are other prominent examples.

3. One would not expect the pyridinium ion to be toxic for alumina. A Lewis diagram reveals the reason:

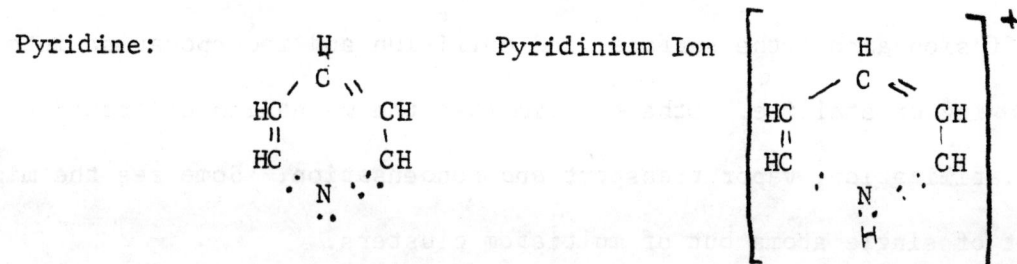

The lone electron pair of pyridine is readily available for bonding on the electron accepting (Lewis Acid) sites of coordinatively unsaturated Al on the Al_2O_3 surface. Addition of the hydrogen shields these electrons and renders the molecule nontoxic. Additional examples are given in Reference 1, Table 1.

4. Zero order kinetics would be expected in those cases where there is a multi-layer deposit of coke. Coke burning would then be dependent only on oxygen partial pressure until coke remaining became less than monolayer. Since typical coke contents of catalysts undergoing regeneration start at from 3 to 15 weight percent, the less than monolayer regime is not a very important one.

5. Three basic steps must be involved:

   a) Transport of the metal component from one place to another on the surface

   b) Agglomeration or coalesence of metal particles

   c) Dispersion or breaking up of metal particles

There is little agreement as to the details of these steps. Some argue that sintering occurs by the detachment of individual atoms from a crystallite, diffusion across the surface, and collision and incorporation into a second, growing crystallite. Others claim that the mechanism of transport is via volatilization, vapor transport and condensation. Some see the migration not of single atoms but of multiatom clusters.

6. If only the Pt function were deactivated and $n-C_5$ the feed, one would see a decreasing rate of conversion of $n-C_5$ to $i-C_5$, the isomerization would not be inhibited. In the limit of complete deactivation one would see no reaction at all, since $n-C_5$ will not isomerize to an appreciable extent on Al_2O_3. If only the Al_2O_3 function were deactivated one would also observe decreasing conversion to $i-C_5$, and perhaps detect the presence of $n-C_5^=$. In the limit of complete deactivation of Al_2O_3 one would observe a product reactant mixture of $n-C_5$ and $n-C_5^=$.

JUL 12 1983